the health care business

the health care business

international evidence on private versus public health care systems

Åke Blomqvist

Associate Professor of Economics
University of Western Ontario
London, Ontario

THE FRASER INSTITUTE
1979

Canadian Cataloguing in Publication Data
Blomqvist, Åke G., 1941-
   The health care business

   Bibliography: p.
   ISBN 0-88975-026-2
   1. Medical care.   2. Medical economics.
3. Insurance, Health.   4. Medical care—
Canada.   5. Insurance, Health—Canada.
I. Fraser Institute, Vancouver, B.C.   II. Title.
RA395.C3B46   362.1'0971   C79-091128-0

Contents

Chapter 1   THE PROBLEM

Chapter 2   THE EVIDENCE

Chapter 3 TOWARDS A SOLUTION

References

Tables

the health care business

Preface

Michael Walker, Director, The Fraser Institute

The objective of Fraser Institute studies is to focus public attention on the role market forces can play in the attainment of economic prosperity for Canadians. A consistent finding in the various studies the Institute has undertaken since 1975 is that scarcity of economic means, even in the context of the apparent bountifulness of the Canadian economy, imposes a necessity to choose between alternatives. To choose between better housing and better food, better education and more amusements, between enjoyment today and investment for the future.

When it comes to expenditures on health care, there is widespread belief that we have no choice. Medical expenses are a must and everything else takes second place. There is, even by those who otherwise would stoutly defend the virtue of freedom of choice, an unwillingness to extend the principle to medical care.

In this book, Professor Åke Blomqvist examines the health care business to determine to what extent we *do* have a choice and whether or not the combination of public and private choice is being intelligently exercised. Are Canadians getting what they want from the collective choice to spend an increasing proportion of GNP on health care? In the course of his analysis of choice in health care, Professor Blomqvist examines the U.S., U.K. and Swedish health care systems as well as Canada's.

His conclusion, leading to a recommendation for a series of sweeping changes to Canada's system of medical insurance, is that in the process of ensuring equal access to medical services, the current Canadian system has become unacceptably inefficient and costly. According to Blomqvist, the response of government to rising costs has been to intervene increasingly in the market for health services—gradually moving the Canadian system closer to the British system of 'choice by bureaucrats'. The result of this trend, he warns, could well be a substantial reduction in the effectiveness of Canada's health services system—currently among the best in the world.

The University of Western Ontario economist sets out a series of changes to current medical and hospital insurance schemes in Canada which would have the effect, over time, of reducing the built-in cost escalation without materially affecting access to medical care. His recommendations are aimed at increasing competition amongst suppliers of medical services, breaking the conflict of interest that medical practitioners currently find themselves in and establishing an economically realistic basis for the delivery of hospital services.

In Blomqvist's opinion, one of the greatest barriers to reforming the current system, and one of the greatest causes of escalating costs, is an unrealistic notion of what constitutes equitable access to health care. This unrealistic notion that "everybody should have access to the best possible medical facilities regardless of cost" is "more expensive than society can afford or would be willing to pay for". "The absurdity of this concept of access can be seen by analogy," says Blomqvist, "with a housing policy that attempted to provide everybody with housing of the best possible kind regardless of cost."

"The equity problem in health care should be viewed in the same way that we view the general problem of welfare—the problem is to ensure that no individual who has the bad luck of getting sick should be denied a 'decent' standard of care for financial reasons. . . ." "The battle cry 'universal access to a minimum level of adequate care' is perhaps not as stirring as 'the best available care for all'. But it is the only sensible one," says Blomqvist.

In analyzing the health care systems presently in place in the U.S., the U.K., Canada and Sweden, Blomqvist draws out a number of interesting points:

• The British system resolves the problem of equal access by promising the best possible care to all and delivering much less. Queues for surgery are lengthy and involve nearly one million at the present time. Meanwhile, an increasing number of those who can afford it choose to be treated outside the National Health Service.

• Canada uses about 31 per cent more hospital days per capita than the U.S.—primarily due to longer average stays in hospital for any given hospitalization.

• Currently, the Canadian health care business (more than $13 billion per year) accounts for a larger proportion of GNP than either agriculture or retail trade.

• The number of hospitalizations per 100,000 people is the same in Canada and the U.S., in spite of the differences in insurance coverage.

• Canada has more physicians per 100,000 (164) than either the U.K. (105) or the U.S. (141).

• Citizens of the U.S. consult doctors more frequently than either Canadians or the British.

• Sweden imposes a deterrent fee of about three dollars per visit to a general practitioner.

• The British National Health Service appears to be less effective in treating pain and disability—as opposed to preventing mortality. "The waiting lines and the apparent existence of untreated 'minor' disease (in the U.K.) may represent an instance where a rigid but economy-minded bureaucratic system prevents people from getting treatment for which they would in fact be willing to pay if they had the choice". *From a Canadian viewpoint, the relevant question is whether we would be willing to pay this kind of price for letting the bureaucrats decide how and when to save money in the health care sector,* rather than making those decisions for ourselves.

• There is no evidence that national life expectancy is increased by larger national expenditures on health care. Most expenditures in the health care sector are not of the "who shall live variety" indicating that there is scope for real choice about how much society should spend on medical care—choice which does not impair survival prospects. In Canada at the present time high mortality diseases, such as heart disease, strokes and cancer, account for only one in seven hospitalizations.

• The extent to which surgeons perform certain procedures—i.e. the incidence of appendectomy, tonsillectomy, hysterectomy—have been shown to *increase* once insurance payment for medical expenses replaces personal payments. Hysterectomy rates per 100,000 of the population (in Saskatchewan) were dramatically *reduced* by the announced intention of the government to investigate the high incidence of this operative procedure.

• In Canada, doctors' salaries do not tend to fall as the number of doctors per 100,000 population increases. However, 23 out of 28 operative procedures ranging from sinus repair to hemorrhoid removal were found to increase as the number of doctors per 100,000 population increased.

• Canada is drifting in the British direction of increased bureaucratization of health care. The symptoms include:

i) Proposals to transfer physicians to a salary system;

ii) Bureaucratic decisions with regard to control of hospital costs, and

iii) Increased interest in the "rationing" of health care resources.

OBJECTIVES

Following his review of the four health care systems, Blomqvist sets out a number of proposals for changes to the Canadian system which have as their objectives:

i) Increasing the efficiency of the Canadian health care delivery system while preserving the equity of access which charac-terizes the present system;

ii) Reducing or eliminating the extent to which government is involved in the dispensing or subsidization of medical services;

iii) Increasing the range of choice available above the minimum required protection. (In the case of automobile insurance, even the provincial auto insurance plans offer people the choice to have or not have comprehensive and collision coverage at various levels of deductibility. Only the third party liability is required by law.); and

iv) Improving future prospects for cost effectiveness to prevent degradation of the standard of care as is currently happening in the United Kingdom.

PROPOSALS

i. A fundamental change should be made to permit competition to develop in the market for health insurance and health services provision, says Professor Blomqvist. There should be a switch from compulsory, subsidized health insurance (provided exclusively by the public sector) to a system of compulsory but unsubsidized health insurance; this could be obtained from any approved insuring institution either in the public or the private sector, either as conventional insurance or in the form of an approved prepayment plan. The first policy measures which would be required would therefore be to put provincial insurance plans on a premium-financed basis, and to develop criteria for approval of private-sector plans. Those criteria should include provision for a major deductible.

ii. The compulsory package should be "minimally adequate" and would resolve the equity problem by providing comprehensive coverage against the cost of *necessary* treatment of major illness with no exclusions or upper limits on the amounts payable. In effect, compulsory insurance should be of the "catastrophe" variety.

iii. There should be no direct, government subsidy for health insurance or health services.

iv. The reduction in government expenditure made possible by the elimination of the general subsidy could be used to compensate for the impact of the cost of compulsory health insurance on low-income families through means of selective changes in the progessive income tax and in the welfare system along the lines of the recent child tax credit initiative.

v. The present system of hospital financing, under which hospitals deliver services on what is essentially a negotiated cost-plus basis, should be modified and replaced with one where services are delivered on the basis of stated fees for individual services or against prepayment.

vi. Health insurance contracts which restrict the patients' right to choose their own doctors should be legalized so as to enable prepayment plans to compete with private and public conventional insurance.

vii. Private insurance should continue to offer insurance supplementary to the minimum package for those who want it (the importance of the supplementary insurance provided by the private sector should clearly depend on the content of the compulsory package). A variety of "high" limits and low deductibles along with co-insurance provisions can be envisaged.

viii. The cost of experimental cures resulting from advanced medical technology should come out of medical research budgets i.e. at no cost to the patients selected and paid for out of general tax revenues on the basis that medical research potentially benefits all of society.

ix. Individuals should be allowed to decide whether or not they want their lives artificially prolonged and to have insurance rates reflect this choice.

x. Insurance payments for institutional care of old age people should be optional: providing that such people are guaranteed a reasonable income (through a public sector pension scheme), they should then be given the choice of deciding whether or not they spend that income on institutional care.

WHAT HAPPENS NEXT?

''Assuming present health insurance arrangements in Canada were to be replaced by legislation requiring everybody to hold a compulsory health insurance package along the lines discussed...what changes would one expect to see in the market for health insurance?'' asks Professor Blomqvist.

A market-oriented health system, Blomqvist argues, would offer a great deal of flexibility in contrast to a national health service:

i. Provincial insurance plans would administer an insurance plan corresponding to the compulsory coverage required by legislation.

ii. Private health insurance agencies would supplement the public plan; because the latter would contain a deductible, private firms might be able to generate additional business by offering policies to cover the deductible.

iii. Because the public insurance plan would not be subsidized, insurance rates would reflect true costs; therefore, private sector insurance firms could start to compete with the public sector insurance firms by themselves offering packages equivalent to the basic compulsory insurance. (This has begun to happen in the case of automobile collision insurance in British Columbia.)

iv. Expected revenue from premiums for the compulsory plan should cover total expected cost of the health services covered under the plan.

v. Some differentiation by risk class might be permitted the public agency when setting premiums. But an alternative to a discriminatory premium structure (e.g. for the elderly) would be legislation regulating the amount of premium discrimination private insurance firms would be allowed.

vi. Competition from prepayment plans of the Health Maintenance Organization type (HMOs) could emerge and similarly from Health Services Organizations (HSOs), or group practices.

vii. Doctors would benefit from health care reform in the direction of more reliance on the market; they would still have a choice between fee-for-service practice or salaried employment either in the public sector or perhaps in private Health Maintenance Organizations. Prepaid group practice might become a more common alternative. A market-oriented system would offer a great deal of flexibility in this sense, in contrast to a national health service system.

viii. In view of the federal-provincial cost-sharing for hospitals in its original form now eliminated, checking burgeoning hospital cost expansion is now a major provincial priority; under the market-oriented alternative there would be no subsidies from the government. Hospitals would be entirely dependent for their revenue on fees-for-service to be paid by individuals or by public or private insurance, or on the income from prepayment arrangements. This would force hospital administrators to adopt more rational principles of cost accounting, more realistic fee structures with doctors etc., with the end result that there would be more efficient choice of diagnostic and treatment procedures in the light of costs. As Blomqvist comments, under the present system, there are no real incentives for efficient choices in this sense.

ix. Under a market-oriented system, one could expect the emergence of smaller, all-purpose hospitals functioning partly as acute-care hospitals and partly as chronic-care/nursing home institutions: there would be much greater flexibility at the local level in terms of the way a "hospital" can operate or be financed.

The Fraser Institute has been pleased to support Professor Blomqvist's work and to publish his findings and thought-provoking suggestions. However, owing to the independence of the author, the views expressed by Professor Blomqvist may or may not conform severally or collectively with those of the members of the Institute.

April, 1979   **Michael Walker**

The Author

Åke Blomqvist was born in Sweden in 1941. After taking an undergraduate degree in business administration at the Stockholm School of Economics, he went to Princeton University for graduate work and was awarded the Ph.D. degree in Economics in 1971. In 1968 he went to the University of Western Ontario, London, Ontario, where he currently is Associate Professor in the Department of Economics.

Professor Blomqvist's writings in the professional journals have focussed on problems of economic development in low-income countries. He has spent several years teaching and doing research in Africa. He is also interested in various problems of micro-economic policy, and has recently written on the issue of pricing gasoline in Canada.

Author's Preface

At the time when the idea of writing this study originally arose, in a conversation with David Laidler, I was relatively unfamiliar with many aspects of the institutional organization of the Canadian health care system. Learning more about it, from the literature and from people working in the field, has been an interesting and rewarding experience. As will become clear below, however, I have not become convinced that the approaches currently being favoured in trying to improve the system are necessarily the most appropriate ones.

The objective of the study is not primarily to derive new analytical or empirical results, but rather to synthesize some of the existing material in the field in the context of answering the broad question whether more reliance should be put on the market mechanism in the efforts currently being made to control health care costs in Canada. I would like to emphasize that I personally think that the standard of medical care, and accessibility to it, are excellent at the present time. What I feel less confident about are some of the methods currently being proposed or implemented to contain costs, and I believe that alternative strategies, which involve the market mechanism to a greater degree, deserve more attention than they have received in recent debate.

I am indebted to a number of people who have helped me in various ways. The Fraser Institute provided the financial support which made the study possible. David Laidler, in addition to providing the initial idea of writing it, has read and commented on several drafts, as has Michael Walker. Drs. Martin Bass and Ian McWhinney provided invaluable expertise on a number of points. Dr. Arnold Aberman gave extensive comments on the manuscript. Stavros Constantinou, Senior Economist with the Canadian Medical Association, not only gave me a great deal of useful statistical information but also a series of very helpful comments and references. Brian Bentley, as my research assistant, did much of the data collection, the statistical work, and in addition served as a patient sounding board for various ideas. A number of people in the Ontario Ministry of Health and the Department of Health and Welfare in Ottawa and at HEW in Washington provided data and helpful discussions. I would particularly like to acknowledge help from Joseph Altopiedi, A. Tarasofsky and Sheila Kelen. Needless to say, none of the persons mentioned above can be held responsible for any of the material contained in the study, and to say that some of them do not share all the views I express probably would be an understatement.

London, Ontario,   A.G. Blomqvist

Chapter 1
THE PROBLEM

I. INTRODUCTION: HEALTH IS BIG BUSINESS

That health services is a major industry in Canada should be readily apparent to anybody who has tried to find his way around in a large city hospital, or has used the yellow pages to pick out a physician to call. That the costs of the health care system are rising rapidly cannot have escaped the notice of even a casual newspaper reader or television watcher. Next to Ministers of Finance and Energy, none have been as vocal in their insistence on the necessity for reducing the rate of growth of consumption and expenditure as the federal or provincial Ministers of Health.

Aggregative statistics relating to the health services sector are indeed impressive. The most recent figures I have found show health services expenditure exceeding 13 billion dollars, or 6.9 per cent of GNP.[1] By comparison, the entire agricultural sector in Canada accounts for only about 4.1 per cent, and retail trade for about the same as health, with 6.8 per cent of GNP.[2]

The health cost explosion
These numbers assume even more significance when one considers their rates of change in recent years. Figures on the rate at which health care expenditure in dollar terms have been increasing in the last few years are not very useful, because to a large extent they reflect general price and cost inflation; price rises have made almost any dollar amount grow rapidly. One gets a more illuminating picture by considering how health care expenditures have changed in relation to GNP. Here the statistics tell us that in 1960, such expenditures accounted for 5.3 per cent of GNP.[3] Given the 1976 figure of nearly 7 per cent, it is clear that over this time period, health care expenditures have been growing considerably faster than other major components of GNP.

The picture is not unique to Canada. Statistics for the U.S.

1

show an increase in the proportion of GNP spent on health care services from 5.2 to 8.6 per cent between 1959-60 and 1975-76.[4] In Britain, where the provision of health services is now almost completely centralized in the public sector, it rose from 3.9 to 5.6 per cent of GNP between 1960 and 1975.[5] While the "expenditure explosion" appears to have moderated somewhat in Canada during the 1970s (relative to GNP, health costs have in fact fallen slightly since 1971-72), a recent OECD study nevertheless showed Canada in fifth place in the world (behind the U.S., Sweden, the Netherlands, and France) when countries are ranked by their share of GNP devoted to health care.[6]

Two major questions

To an economist who is confronted with the numbers just discussed, two major kinds of questions immediately present themselves. *First,* can economic analysis contribute to understanding why Canadian and other societies are allocating a rapidly increasing share of their productive resources (manpower, capital, etc.) to the provision of health services, rather than to the production of other goods and services? *Second,* and this is the question relevant to policymaking, do we need to do something about it? In other words, is it the case that an *excessive* amount of resources is being allocated to health services provision in the sense that those resources would be more valuable to society in other uses? I briefly discuss those questions in the next two sections.

II. ECONOMIC ANALYSIS AND RISING HEALTH EXPENDITURE

A. *"IT IS NOT AN ECONOMIC PROBLEM BECAUSE THERE IS NO CHOICE"*

Whether or not economic analysis can make a significant contribution to explaining the rise in health expenditure depends a great deal on the degree of *choice* that society has in providing health services. Those who do not think there is much, argue somewhat as follows: "At a given time, with given medical technology (I will come back to the meaning of that phrase later), there is a 'best' treatment to which a person with a particular health problem is entitled. Given technology, the doctor has little choice with respect to recommending or not recommending hospitalization for whatever length of time; performing or not performing surgery, and with respect to the type of medication he prescribes. Similarly, he has little or no choice with respect to performing or ordering diagnostic tests of different kinds for a given patient, and so on.''

"On the health services production side," the argument continues, "there is also little choice with regard to the inputs required to produce a given mix of services. Given the population and its health services requirements, we will need exactly so many GPs and specialists, so many hospital beds, so many nurses and laboratory technicians, so many x-ray machines and intensive care units, etc., and we cannot substitute various inputs for each other if we want to produce the given output of required services.''

Explaining the health cost explosion if there is no choice
If the "no choice" view of the world is true, how are we to explain the observed rapid increase in health services consumption discussed above? One could think of three major types of explanations.

Age and life style
First, required health services consumption may have risen because the number of old people relative to the total population has risen, and old people on the average need to consume more health services. It has also been hypothesized that over the long run there has been an increase in the incidence of various types of "life style" related conditions: heart disease related to overeating and lack of physical activity in sedentary work; heart, lung and liver disease related to smoking and excessive drinking; various types of injury as a result of auto accidents.[7] The requirements for health services to cope with those kinds of conditions appear to have increased secularly, offsetting decreases in requirements related to infectious diseases which now can be treated relatively cheaply or against which

protection can be had through vaccination (tuberculosis, poliomyelitis, measles, are examples).

Increasing relative costs and inflexible manpower requirements

A second type of explanation is cast in terms of the rising costs of the inputs into the provision of medical services, i.e., rising wages of doctors, nurses, and hospital personnel in general, rising costs of equipment and drugs, etc. In one version of this argument, it is observed that health services provision generally speaking is a relatively labour-intensive activity, i.e., the proportion of total cost accounted for by wages and salaries is higher in this type of activity than it is for the production of most other goods and services. Since in industrialized countries there is a strong tendency for wages and salaries to rise relative to the prices of other (non-labour) inputs, it stands to reason that the cost of labour-intensive services will rise faster than the costs of other goods and services. This would help explain why health expenditures have not only been growing rapidly but more rapidly than expenditure on other things.

This basic tendency will be exacerbated if, as is often asserted, there is little flexibility in the mix of inputs needed to produce health services. Lack of flexibility means that machines cannot be substituted for men (i.e., more laboratory equipment, computers for diagnosis and record-keeping, larger hospitals, and fewer doctors, nurses, orderlies, and technicians) when the latter become more and more expensive relative to the former.

Medical technology

A third set of ''non-economic'' factors, finally, which is often used to explain rising health care costs, is the advance in medical technology. Technological advance by itself may, on the one hand, have a tendency to reduce cost and expenditure (e.g., vaccination against poliomyelitis certainly must have saved considerable amounts of money by eliminating the cost of treatment of those who would otherwise have contracted it). On the other hand, it may raise costs if it makes available new and more effective treatment of various conditions, although at high cost. Examples of the latter would be open-heart surgery, organ transplants, renal dialysis, and radiation treatment against cancer. While we cannot know for sure which of these two effects has had the most impact, the scattered information that is available on the cost of some of the new and advanced techniques certainly makes it plausible that the increase in total health care cost due to their more widespread use has outweighed cost savings due to cheaper methods of treating some other conditions.

It is also possible that advancing medical technology may interact with the first factor mentioned above, i.e., the advancing average age of the population, to increase total health care expenditure. With more effective health care, more people will survive to old age and therefore incur more health services costs than would be the case had they not survived. Hence one can argue that, paradoxically, one reason for the increasing total cost of health care is the successful advances in health care technology: those advances have increased people's life expectancy, but have thereby also increased the amount of health care services that the average individual will require.

The ideology of medical practice and its consequences

While there may not be anybody who would argue that the element of choice in the health services area is so unimportant that the factors just discussed *completely* explain the observed increases in health care costs, they are nevertheless the central ones in the views of many people. Perhaps it would be fair to argue that they are typical of many medical practitioners. The ideology of medical practice, of course, has always tended to put the healing of the patient above all other considerations. If one accepts that ideology, the idea that in the event of sickness, every individual is entitled to the best available treatment, given existing technology and regardless of cost and ability to pay, follows as a natural consequence.

In the face of this ideology what is to be done about rapidly rising health care expenditures?

Essentially nothing: if advances in medical technology, an aging population, and rising costs of manpower and material inputs into health services production conspire to rapidly raise total expenditures, so be it. The rising cost is simply the price we pay for adhering to the ideal that every sick person is entitled to the best available treatment. The alternative would be to abandon that ideal, and to many people in this group, that is an unacceptable alternative. To quote the Task Force on the Cost of Health Services in Canada:

> " ...it may be pertinent to conceptualize the situation which would obtain under ideal conditions of medical care:...each person would receive optimum medical diagnostic and treatment services when indisposed and these would be available without regard for his socioeconomic status or locality...."[8]

B. THE ECONOMIST'S VIEW—
THE NECESSITY TO CHOOSE

Some puzzling questions

From the viewpoint of an economist looking at this area, the analysis above of the structure and growth of the health services industry raises a number of puzzling questions. An economist's basic approach to the problem would be somewhat as follows. We know that people value long life and good health, and presumably health services are used because they contribute to those objectives. But people also attach value to other things: food, housing, recreation, for example. Given that the amounts of productive resources in the form of manpower, capital equipment, natural resources, etc., are limited, we must accept the fact that if we use more resources for health services provision, there will be fewer left to produce the other goods and services. We could, after all, train more architects and fewer doctors; build fewer hospitals and more private homes. Given this fact, we must make *choices;* in particular, we must decide how much health services to produce rather than other things.

Health care versus everything else?

How are we to make this choice? As just noted, the 'we have no choice' view suggests that we make it by putting enough resources into health services provision so that every person can be given the best treatment available, given existing technology. This done, we can allocate the rest between food, housing, recreation, etc.

But if we use this procedure for health services, could we not equally well use it for housing, for example? We could have architects tell us what is the best available housing, given current technology (wall-to-wall carpeting, central air-conditioning, fireplaces in the living room and family room, kidney-shaped swimming pool and gas barbecue in the back yard) and make it a national priority to provide every person with such housing. Why do we not do this? Because it would cost too much, obviously, i.e., it would leave too few resources to produce other things.

But then, do we not have the same problem with a policy of providing the ''best available'' health services to every person who needs it? Looking at the problem in a different light, how do we define ''equal access to the best available medical care''? Clearly, we cannot have a hospital with a full range of advanced equipment in every town; equally clearly, we cannot have as many primary care physicians as would be required in order to guarantee that everybody would be able to see one in his neighbourhood without any waiting time. It would obviously be too expensive to have everybody in the population undergo a major medical checkup every year on a routine basis, or to provide enough periodic retraining of doctors to ensure that they would all be equally familiar with the latest medical technology. Yet all of these things could reasonably be required as part of the definition of universal access to the best available treatment.

Face the facts
The basic point has now been made (perhaps to excess): *so long as productive resources are limited, and so long as we can think of new ways of spending money on the health services system to further improve the quality of health care, or to make it even more readily available to all individuals, we as a society must somehow make a choice:* do we want more health services even though it must mean less of other things? References to some absolute standard, such as equal access to best available care, in the economist's view simply reflects our unwillingness to face that fact.

The choice-making process
Thus an economist looking at the process that has produced the explosion in health care expenditures in the industrialized

countries discussed above would focus his attention on the way in which those choices were made, and by whom. Evidently, this is not to deny the importance of the factors discussed earlier, i.e., an aging population, advances in technology, and rising costs of inputs into the health services sector: those factors will certainly affect the choices, regardless of who makes them. However, the hypothesis of interest is that the form of the decision-making process whereby resources are allocated to the health services sector has also contributed to the rise in costs. Moreover, as will be argued later on, the nature of the decision-making process is important in assessing whether the choices represented an *efficient* allocation of resources.

III. THE MARKET FOR HEALTH SERVICES: THE DEMAND SIDE

A. WHAT'S SO GOOD ABOUT THE MARKET?

How a market works

As most people will be aware, economists spend a great deal of their time expounding the virtues of "the impersonal forces of supply and demand" as a mechanism for guiding the allocation of society's scarce productive resources, i.e., for making the sorts of *choices* that were referred to above. Most people are probably also familiar with the essential elements of the supply-demand model. Briefly, it describes a process through which no single individual or agency decides how much of a given good or service is going to be produced in the society. Instead there is a *market* for it where consumers are free to buy as much of it as they please, at a given price, and suppliers can put as much for sale as they please. If the total quantity demanded exceeds the quantity supplied, say, tendencies toward shortages may develop and consumers may begin bidding up prices in order to be able to get as much as they want, or, more realistically, producers may find that they can raise prices and still be able to sell as much as they want. In either case, the "market price" will begin to rise.

Consumers, finding the good or service more expensive, will tend to demand a smaller quantity at a higher price. Producers will find it more profitable to produce and will increase production, and if at a higher price the profits on invested capital become higher in this particular industry than in others, new investment will take place and new firms may enter the market. The decrease in quantity demanded and increase in quantity supplied will tend to wipe out the excess demand, and in "equilibrium", the market price will be such that the quantity demanded by consumers matches the amount offered by producers, and the profitability of firms in this industry is about the same as in others.

In "mixed" economies, such as the Canadian one, the resource allocation decisions for most goods and services are made in this implicit way through the individual consumption and production decisions of households and firms, without the need for the large-scale planning bureaucracy which fulfills this role in centrally-planned economies. For most goods and services, the market system functions reasonably well when it is left to its own devices: when there is unrestricted competition between firms, only those firms that can produce efficiently (i.e., at low cost) and charge relatively low prices will be left in the market, and the quantities produced will match those that individual consumers freely choose to buy at those prices.

Individual preferences the basis of efficiency
Before discussing the question of the applicability of the supply-demand model in the context of resource allocation to health services, it may be useful to consider briefly the underlying philosophical reasons why economists, by and large, tend to be strong supporters of the market mechanism. In part, it may simply reflect a general distrust of the efficiency and flexibility of large-scale bureaucracies in solving the extremely complex problems that arise in resource allocation. More fundamentally, however, it springs from the notion that a "good" system of resource allocation should be one in which various goods and services not only are produced efficiently, i.e., at the lowest possible cost, but also in relative quantities which are as responsive as possible to individual wants or preferences. To anticipate the future discussion, it is quite possible that the value which consumers attach to some of the services produced in the Canadian health care sector is

less than the cost of producing them. It will be argued that, if this is so, society would be better off if those services were eliminated and the resources transferred to producing something which consumers value more highly, such as better housing, for example. The moral of the story is that the use of productive resources in *any* sector can only be justified if the good or service produced in the sector is as valuable or more valuable to consumers, as the goods and services which could be produced with those resources if they were used in other sectors. There is no reason why health services should be an exception to this rule.

Markets reflect consumer values

Now the discussion in the preceding paragraph only establishes a general principle regarding efficient allocation of resources between alternative uses; it does not by itself necessarily lead to the conclusion that the market mechanism is always the best way to achieve this allocation. The reader no doubt realizes, however, that under circumstances when a competitive market can be expected to function reasonably well in other respects, it also provides an effective way of bringing about an efficient resource allocation in the above sense. It does so because competition between suppliers will ensure that goods and services are offered for sale at prices that reflect the cost of producing them, and the amounts produced will depend on the consumers' valuation of the goods since they themselves have determined how much they will buy at that price. Thus when it works well, the market mechanism provides an effective signalling device through which consumers' relative valuation of different goods and services is transmitted to producers, and the allocation of productive resources is indirectly guided, in a rough way, by the individual preferences of the consumers.

Do markets work in health care provision?

The discussion above is only a background, however. The real issue to be addressed in the remainder of this chapter is not whether the market mechanism in general constitutes a useful device for allocating resources, but whether it does so for the health services sector in particular. Those who oppose a greater reliance on the market in the health services context do not necessarily argue against the general principle of letting resources be allocated through the market. Rather, they argue that health services have special characteristics which make individual consumer preferences an inappropriate allocation criterion, or that the nature of health services production for various reasons will preclude effective competition between suppliers, and so on. In the next few sections I will discuss some of those objections by considering how the demand for and supply of health services would be determined in a more or less unrestricted market, and I will also discuss various institutional devices through which the market might be made to function more in accordance with the competitive ideal; I will finally address a question which was not considered above, but which has always had considerable importance in the public debate regarding health services, namely whether a market-determined allocation would be "unfair", e.g., in the sense of denying low-income people access to adequate health care.

B. ARE HEALTH SERVICES A "PUBLIC GOOD"?

There are a number of versions of the argument that health care has special characteristics which make individual preferences an unreliable guide for deciding what constitutes an appropriate level of health care production from the viewpoint of society as a whole. One version proceeds from the premise that health services are so-called public goods and as such should be financed through the tax system rather than from proceeds of individual sales of services.

A public good is...
From a technical point of view, a public good has the characteristic that when some of it is provided, several individuals, perhaps all individuals in society, will benefit *jointly* from its provision. Thus, if I buy a bag of peanuts or the services of a tax lawyer, I alone will benefit from the eating or the tax savings, respectively. But consider services such as those of law enforcement agencies and the judicial system, or from national defence or fire protection, or from snow removal

off public highways, or from a city sewer system: each of us benefits from those services, yet we cannot individually decide how much to "buy" because we all have to "consume" the same amounts. In order for sufficient resources to be allocated to services of this kind, all the beneficiaries have to get together and agree on the contribution of each to the total cost; in reality, of course, these agreements are made implicitly through the tax system, and the costs of public goods are defrayed from the tax revenue of local, provincial or federal governments.

With respect to health services the argument is sometimes made that the benefits from them, in the form of "good health", are not confined to those individuals who make use of the services, but that we all benefit jointly from a healthy population. The implication would be that resources should not be allocated to this sector solely on the basis of the "willingness-to-pay" for the services of the actual users. Rather, it is held, all members of society should jointly decide on the value they would attach to both their own and everybody else's consumption of different amounts of health services and then tax themselves accordingly. The production of health services would be financed out of the resulting revenue. According to this school of thought, a market allocation, under which the level of health services would depend only on the willingness to pay of actual users, would lead to an underproduction of services.

The special case of contagious disease
For a certain type of health services, there is no doubt about the validity of this argument: those services designed to prevent the spread of various forms of contagious disease. Thus, for example, I will benefit if you, and everybody else, is inoculated against poliomyelitis or diphtheria. Not only the patient himself, but also those who would have come into contact with him, will benefit from screening and isolation of active cases of tuberculosis. If "health services" are defined broadly to include the maintenance of a sanitary environment, one can also include such things as garbage collection and the maintenance of safe sewerage and water-supply systems among health services which have the character of public goods. For

all of these, it appears inadvisable to leave the "purchase decision" up to the individual, since the resulting decisions would be made without taking into account the benefits or costs conferred on everybody else.† In actual fact, the types of services just described are not only publicly financed out of tax revenue, but in some cases are also covered by legislation making "consumption" mandatory.

During the first half of this century, various forms of infectious disease did indeed constitute the most important type of health problem. And, there is no doubt that the enormous advances which have been made in terms of reducing mortality and improving the general health of the population since then, have in large part been due to measures such as widespread inoculation and improvements in sanitary conditions. There is also no doubt that to a large extent these developments depended on public-sector initiatives and could not have come about as effectively through the market mechanism.‡

New diseases prompt different attitudes toward public goods

If one looks at the health services being consumed today, however, those which are aimed at controlling contagious disease or at maintaining a sanitary environment, constitute only a small fraction of the total. The large scale epidemics of infectious disease which were the big killers of an earlier era have now been replaced in this role by cancer and diseases of the circulatory system.[9] While there would presumably exist a wide agreement that the taxpayers' money could legitimately be used to finance inoculation from which the whole community would jointly benefit, the same agreement might not exist with respect to cancer and heart disease: treatment of such forms of disease benefit those who suffer from it and their families, but is of no direct benefit to anybody else. Less dramatically, the taxpayer may be even less happy paying for

---

† Editor's Note: However, as Professor Blomqvist has indicated at several points in the book, that a service is a "public good" does not necessarily imply that it should be *provided* by the public sector.

‡ Editor's Note: In terms of disease control, while governments have clearly played a substantive role in administering inoculations, once the vaccine has been discovered, there is no evidence to suggest that government initiatives have been particularly important in originating vaccines or cures.

removing the tonsils of the brat next door who seems perfectly healthy, or for an operation on the boss's varicose veins in order to make him look better on the tennis court. The benefits of those kinds of health services, if any, again go to the patients themselves but are of little concern to the community at large. The examples could be multiplied, but the point has been made: apart from those designed to control contagious disease, and which should therefore appropriately be produced by public health departments, health services consumed today are by and large private goods, and the argument for transferring financial responsibility for their provision to the public sector cannot validly be made on this basis.

Before leaving this point, mention should be made of a different, somewhat more subtle, argument that is sometimes used to support the case for tax-financed health services in general. The thrust of this argument is that because we have a public welfare system, the taxpayer has an interest in keeping people healthy enough to earn enough money to stay off the welfare rolls. Tax-financed health services may be seen as contributing to that objective. Simplifying the argument, it may be taken to say that we may get back in reduced welfare payments some of the money spent on health services.

As a strictly logical proposition, this point is perfectly correct. Two qualifying comments are in order, however. First, it is not clear that better access to health care for potential welfare candidates will in fact reduce the future tax burden on the rest of the population. For example, the "cheapest" solution, in this sense, to the problem of the high cost of treating alcoholism may be to let alcoholics drink themselves to death quickly. In other words, easy access to medical care now may merely result in large future costs to take care of people who otherwise would have died.

Second, the quantitative significance of any net effect on the tax burden of the rest of the population, it seems to me, must be fairly small in any case. Even if people have to pay for their own health services (or for their own health insurance), one would expect them to seek treatment for conditions so severe that they would be incapable of earning a living if they didn't get treatment. While in some cases people do not know how serious a particular disease is and hence may get seriously ill because they did not seek care for that reason, the number of such cases must be very small, and not all such patients would seek care even if the cost were zero, i.e., if health services were tax-financed. At most, the point is a minor qualification to the principle that health services must be regarded as private goods.

C. WILLINGNESS-TO-PAY:
FOR SERVICES OR INSURANCE?

Demand for health services depends on chance

In the earlier discussion, it was argued that one of the advantages of the market mechanism was its ability to make the allocation of resources responsive to individual preferences. The amount of any good or service provided through the market depends on people's willingness to pay for it: the number of barbers and barbershops, say, depends on how much money people freely choose to pay for haircuts, given their valuation of haircuts and other goods, and given their incomes.

Now with respect to something like haircuts, it may be meaningful to speak of an individual equilibrium rate of consumption: given the price of haircuts, the individual can adjust his consumption towards this rate, and as long as the cost stays unchanged he will leave it there. But with respect to something like health services, it can be argued that the idea of an equilibrium consumption level for an *individual* does not really make sense, since the question whether or not you will consume them is, to a large extent, a matter of luck. If you get sick, you will; otherwise, you will not.

Because of the unpredictability of an individual's need for consumption of health care, many people argue that even though by and large health services are not public goods in the sense discussed in the previous section, the allocation of resources to this field cannot be left to the market because to do this would be ethically unacceptable. Market allocation would deny medical care to people who did not have enough money, or who could not borrow enough, to pay for it if they should have the bad luck to get sick.

Catastrophic versus discretionary health problems

In assessing this argument, it might first of all be observed that in any given year it would of course only pertain to a relatively small group of people. Even though most families have *some* medical expenses in a given year, the vast majority will spend less than five hundred dollars, say, which is a great deal less than they will spend on food or housing, and no more than it would cost to deal with a serious breakdown of the family car. Furthermore, much of this expenditure will be incurred to deal with relatively minor and, in some cases, "discretionary" health problems: cuts and bruises, twisted ankles, bad colds or headaches, minor elective surgery, etc. For these types of people and health services, it would seem no more unethical to let individuals pay for their own consumption than it would for their consumption of food, housing and transport.

For the few individuals who have a major "serious" health problem, however, the cost may greatly exceed what they would be able to pay for out of their own resources. Would an unrestricted market system deny medical care to such people just because they "do not have the money"?

The ethical objection

In some cases, it undeniably would, even though the existence of various charitable organizations and public welfare in any system means that at least in cases of serious illness, some care would generally be given. But for most people in a modern society, it would not. It would rather mean that they would get care as long as their insurance company were "willing to pay" for it: under a market system, most people would choose to be covered by health insurance, at their own initiative or as part of their employment contract. As the evidence in Chapter Two will show, this is indeed what has happened in the U.S. The existence of private health insurance, therefore, to a large extent removes the force of the ethical objection to reliance on the market. What remains is the possibility that a small minority of the population would choose not to be covered by health insurance, or would choose to be "inadequately" covered. It is a different matter that considerations of social justice might be used to justify policies designed to improve the protection of this minority (which, after all, will include individuals who are "bad risks" through no fault of their own, or those who consider themselves too poor to afford health insurance), and I will return to this problem at a later stage. The point being made here simply is that through the market for health insurance, the vast majority of people would be perfectly capable of providing protection for themselves against financially disastrous medical costs, and would not have to be denied care for financial reasons, even in case of serious illness, with expensive treatment.

D. INSURANCE AND CHOICE

Even if it is granted that the existence of insurance does much to remove the force of the ethical objection to relying on the market for the provision of health services, there are some people who maintain that this solution amounts to throwing out the baby with the bath water. The argument goes somewhat as follows. Since productive resources in society are scarce, when more resources are allocated to the consumption and production of some particular commodity, less of them will be available to be used for producing other ones. In a market system where the allocation is supposed to be guided by individual consumers, recognition of the fact of scarcity is forced on the individual by his limited income and the fact that he has to pay for what he consumes. When he chooses to buy more haircuts, for example, he will have to pay for them himself and will thus have less money left to spend on other things. Indirectly, therefore, market prices provide individuals with the information that is necessary in order for them to make choices which in the aggregate become consistent with society's limitations on resources available.

Insurance makes health services free
But consider now an individual who is covered by insurance and faces the decision whether to consume more health care. If he chooses to do so, the insurance will pay for it, and he will

not have less money to spend on other things. Thus, the argument goes, when individuals are insured, market prices do not serve the function of making individuals realize that, taken together, they have to choose between health services and other things; consumption decisions by insured individuals will be made as if health services were "free".

This argument does indeed have considerable merit, as far as it goes, and probably contains a good part of the explanation for the rapid increase in the money spent on health services consumption in societies such as Canada where virtually everybody has a more or less uniform, comprehensive health insurance. What it neglects, however, is the element of choice that would exist in a market system where an individual would have the freedom to decide on the extent and form of his own *insurance coverage*.

Insurance indirectly reflects costs of health care

If health insurance is privately provided, it must of course be true that the total premium income has to be at least enough to pay for the cost of insured services plus administration costs and to earn a return on the capital invested in the insurance firms. On the other hand, if there is a reasonable amount of competition in the insurance industry, the premium income should be no higher than is required to pay those costs and to earn no more than a "normal" return. If the return were higher, it would be profitable for other firms to enter the market, and there would be increased competition between firms for customers with a tendency for premium levels to fall as a result. Thus in a well-functioning market, premium levels would on the average reflect the cost of providing the insured services.

Health insurance is a conditional purchase choice

Hence the real choice made by an insured individual is not made at the time when he falls ill and makes use of his insurance to pay for specific health services: it was rather made earlier at the time when he decided to insure himself against the cost of those services. At that time, the individual had to consider his *conditional* valuation of different health services relative to other goods and services. In other words, he had to ask himself a question like: given the risk that I will fall ill, how much am I willing to give up of other goods and services today in order to be able to "consume" specific types of health services in case I fall ill? In other words, how extensive should my health insurance coverage be, given the price of health insurance? But if the prices of different types of health insurance roughly correspond to the expected costs of the insured services, then an individual who is deciding on the extent of his insurance coverage is in effect choosing between health services and other things, just as an individual contemplating the purchase of a haircut is effectively choosing between haircuts and other things, given his limited income. Hence the existence of insurance does not negate the basic principle that the choice between health services and other things is in fact made by the individual himself. The only difference is that it is the price of insurance, rather than the prices of the insured services themselves, which provides the information on which the choice will be made.

How much choice?
In the real world, how much choice does the individual have in this sense? To begin with, it is clear that much of the answer depends on the flexibility of the health insurance industry. If all that they offer is one standard comprehensive insurance package, then there is not much the individual consumer can do: even if he acts in such a way as to reduce his own expected level of health services consumption, this will not have any appreciable impact on the average consumption of the population as a whole, and hence his premium costs will not fall. Suppose, however, that there is flexibility in the type of insurance package offered for sale, and correspondingly, in insurance premiums. There are then various ways in which an individual could save by attempting to reduce his consumption. He could try to buy cheaper hospitalization insurance by covering himself only for the cost of a ward (as opposed to semi-private or private room). He might find a cheaper insurance contract which would exclude coverage of minor ailments for which no hospitalization or expensive treatment were necessary, and/or coverage of the services of a family doctor. More generally (and realistically), he could get a

contract with a deductible, i.e., under which he himself would take responsibility for all health care expenditures up to some specific amount per year or per disease episode. Some people, in fact, might choose to insure themselves only for the cost of "catastrophic" illness.

Of course, by choosing to reduce the extent to which he is covered for various types of health expenditure, the person is not necessarily deciding that he will not consume those services at all: he may subsequently decide, e.g., to continue visiting his family doctor in order to be treated for minor ailments. However, if he feels that he has some real choice with respect to the use of those services, he is expecting that on average, he will be spending less money on them if he has to pay the cost out of his own pocket than he would be spending if he were paying for them indirectly through his insurance premium. The moral is this: if you want to keep the option open to save money by consuming less of what you consider "discretionary" health services, do not insure yourself against the cost of those services.

Insurance risk and the "right-to-die"

Another interesting alternative might arise from the recently discussed "right-to-die" legislation in Ontario, under which it is proposed that a person should be able to write in his will a clause to the effect that he would not wish to have his life artificially prolonged by extraordinary measures. Such a clause would reduce the expected cost of health services for this individual, and may make it possible for him to obtain less expensive insurance.

Finally, if insurance companies were reasonably able to discriminate between people in different risk classes, there are some things an individual could do in order to improve his risk rating: exercise more, eat less, smoke less, drink less alcohol, not drive a red sports car (to borrow an example from the auto insurance industry), and so on. The individual might not *like* to do these things; but since these actions are, in effect, partial substitutes for health services consumption in producing good health, he may still think it worthwhile to engage in them if the price of health services goes high enough. Discrimination by risk might of course be considered inequitable for individuals who are in high-risk classes through no fault of their own, and I will return later to the question whether this problem can be dealt with in a market system. But many risks are self-imposed, and incentives on people to avoid such risks may become an increasingly important way of controlling health care costs.

IV. HEALTH SERVICES AND THE DOCTOR

A. WHEN THE EXPERTS CHOOSE FOR YOU

The discussion in the previous section concerns ways in which the *individual consumer* might be able and willing to exercise choices with respect to his health services consumption. There are many who argue, however, that the consumer's choices are not the really important ones in this area, and that the impact that they would have on total health services costs would not be very large. Instead, the major choices and decisions to be concerned with are the ones made by *doctors*.[9A]

Why are so many of the decisions in this area made by doctors? Obviously because many of the decisions relating to health require specialized knowledge. Even if the consumer (or patient) really makes the decisions himself, it would certainly be in the patient's interest to pay for the information and advice that a trained doctor can provide before making them. This way of looking at the process draws attention to the fact that doctors (and especially the family doctors, or GPs, or primary care physicians) not only serve the function of actually providing treatment to patients; they also must act, to a large extent, as providers of information and advice with respect to health services consumption.

A conflict of interest?
In a system where doctors are paid on a fee-for-service basis, this situation obviously provides the possibility for a potential conflict of interest. The doctors are asked to give the patient advice on the question 'how much health services', including the services of the doctors themselves, that he ought to consume. Of course, this type of situation is not unique to the medical field,

21

but exists to a greater or lesser exent for all sorts of goods and services where the consumption choice requires specialized knowledge. The tax lawyer will advise you on the amount of his services he thinks you ought to use; an interior decorator or a building contractor tells you what he thinks you ought to do to your home and how much of his services you ought to buy. Your auto mechanic, like your cardiac surgeon, may explain to you the dire consequences of not having him do a valve job.

How the market resolves conflict of interest

How are such potential conflicts of interest resolved in a market system? Partly, the answer must be that they are not. The consumer just clenches his teeth and pays. But there are some checks: an auto mechanic who charges high prices and does shoddy work will acquire a bad reputation, as will a tax lawyer who keeps losing his cases. The consumer may spend time getting advice and information from several sources, and he has some choice of less expensive substitute services: if the tax lawyer is too expensive, he can go to H & R Block, and if an authorized car dealer charges too much to make car repairs the neighbourhood mechanic is often a good substitute, even if he does not have class A qualifications. In part, the conflicts may be reduced by contractual arrangements: instead of charging for the actual amount of his services after the event, the building contractor may give a prior quote and himself take the risk of having to put in more time than estimated, or paying higher prices for materials. Some goods and services are sold with guarantees of performance, or money-back-unless-satisfied provisions. The tax lawyer may take a cut of the money he saves rather than charge on a fee-for-service basis. The more expensive the goods and services involved, the greater the extent to which it pays the consumer to get as much information as possible, to contract for the price in advance, to insist on a guarantee, or to pay by results as in the case of the tax lawyer.

Note that in all these cases, it is his own money that the consumer is spending. As was discussed before, in the case of health services, he is most of the time spending the insurance company's money. The only parallel case that I can think of is auto repair after an accident; the typical procedure here is for the auto insurance company to insist on several independent estimates, and yet, as anybody having had the experience can probably testify, many mechanics will want to know whether it is an insurance company that will pay, and the cost to insurance companies of auto repairs has been rising rapidly. The same thing, not surprisingly, has been happening to collision insurance rates.

The health services industry, and particularly doctors' services, in several ways represent an extreme case of this problem. First of all, the specialized knowledge doctors provide is complex and changing rapidly. Secondly, the practice of getting independent estimates of the cost of treatment has not been used partly because of the traditional reluctance of physicians to openly criticize each other's judgement. Finally, the price you would pay for making the wrong choice with respect to health services may be a good deal higher than being stuck with an interior decoration you do not like or having your car break down because you picked a cheap garage to fix it.

The role of ethics
In many respects, the individual patient-consumer in a market system does not have much of a chance to take actions to protect himself against "excessive" charges for "unnecessary" or substandard work, nor does he have the choice to use less expensive substitute services: as far as the practice of medicine goes, there are only class A mechanics and no H & R Blocks, only tax lawyers. At the same time, of course, the medical profession has always had a reputation for high ethical standards with respect to quality of work, and also with respect to taking the patient's general welfare into account, including a concern for not having uninsured low-income patients spend "too much" money on high-priced services if cheaper substitutes were available. Economists working on the pricing of physician services have tended to downplay the importance of the ethical motive relative to economic self-interest, but it seems plausible to believe that medical ethics has often been an important force in the provision of reasonable health services for low-income people in market-oriented systems.

To the extent they have existed, the checks against the exploitation of consumer ignorance in the health services field in market-oriented systems in fact have been primarily ethical.

There has not been much in the way of contractual arrangements to protect the consumer: medical services do not come with a warranty, and the cost of many types of services is not agreed upon in advance. The fees charged for the services do not vary with the degree of success of the treatment.

But the ethical restraints on the doctors' behaviour as service suppliers and medical advisors rested on the traditional relationship between doctor and patient, and probably was most likely to work well in a situation where the financial burden of exploiting consumer ignorance would have been borne by the very patient for whose welfare the doctor was supposed to be concerned. In a market system where most services are paid for by health insurance, it is no longer so much a question of the doctor exploiting the patient's ignorance; the question rather concerns the doctor exploiting the ignorance of the insurance company, sometimes even doing so jointly with the patient. Since there is not a "traditional doctor-insurance company" relationship to fall back on, there will be less of an incentive on the doctor to take cost into account when making decisions regarding treatment recommended for a patient, or in deciding what treatment he himself will administer and the price he will charge.

B. INTERDEPENDENT SUPPLY AND DEMAND

Considerations such as those just discussed have led a number of economists to argue that in a situation with widespread comprehensive health insurance, the traditional supply-demand model loses its relevance, because the demand and supply of health services are interdependent. On the one hand, the supply of physician services depends on the number of doctors in the system and the number of hours they are willing to work. On the other hand, the demand for those same services is also seen as being determined by the doctors. If the patient is covered by comprehensive insurance, the simplest strategy for him may be to let the doctor decide what health services he should consume, both in the form of physician services and hospital services. In such a system, the amounts produced and consumed, and the total amount of health services expenditure, depend almost exclusively on decisions by the doctors.

Doctors' incomes versus patients' health
The amounts of physician services produced, and the fees
charged per unit of service, are seen as determined by the income
aspirations of doctors on the one hand, and on the other hand,
their desire to conform to the medical ethic, i.e., to provide those
services which are in the best interests of the patients' health, at a
reasonable cost. But those objectives may not be mutually
consistent: the only way to reach some "target income" without
working very long hours may be to raise fees; or if there are few
patients per doctor, to provide more services per patient than is
really warranted in the interest of the patient's health. Similarly,
the amount of hospital services (including tests, etc.) that the
doctors decide to have their patients consume is seen as
depending not only on their assessment of what is good for the
patients' health, but also on the amount of income that
hospitalization or hospital tests will generate for the doctor:
comprehensive insurance will reimburse the doctor for services
such as interpretation of tests, visits to patients in hospital,
and so on.

Consumer sovereignty out the window?
If this view of the world is correct, there is little reason to expect
that the allocation of resources to the health services system will
bear any relationship to consumers' "willingness to pay" for
them, i.e., to their valuation of health services relative to other
goods and services. The consumers' "freedom of choice", which
was held out in the previous section as one of the most important
advantages of the market system, of course becomes meaningless
if the patient cannot get the information he needs in order to
assess the value of health services in producing the things he
ultimately wants, such as a long life, absence of disability and
pain, etc. Instead, the market mechanism becomes a device
through which the medical profession is allowed to practice
medicine in accordance with the objectives and interests of its
members, with little guarantee that those objectives will be
responsive to the desires of the patients who, after all, are paying
the bill.

Is this an accurate view of the world? In Chapter Two, I will
discuss some Canadian evidence which indicates that doctors in
provinces with few patients per physician are able to earn at least

as high an income as those in provinces with many patients per doctor. A famous study of hysterectomies performed in Saskatchewan[10] showed a very noticeable decline in the proportion of "medically unjustified" operations after the doctors became aware that such a study was going on. There is evidence from both the U.S. and Canada (again discussed in Chapter Two) that the rate of so-called "elective surgery" is significantly influenced by the number of doctors per head in a population: if there are many doctors, there are many operations.

While this evidence can be interpreted in more than one way, it certainly is consistent with the idea that North American doctors are able to "create the demand" for their own services, and many people believe that this ability has contributed in an important way to the rapidly rising costs of health care and to public dissatisfaction with the health care system in both Canada and the U.S. But it is important to note that these are also systems in which the prevailing method of paying the doctors has been the fee-for-service system, and in which comprehensive health insurance has become widespread, partly through public provision of insurance. The importance of this factor has been carefully and convincingly demonstrated for the Canadian case by Robert Evans, who found remarkable rates of increase in the net earnings of physicians in all Canadian provinces at the time when comprehensive insurance was introduced.[11] In the next section I will argue that the market mechanism, if left to its own devices without restrictions on competition, is likely to itself produce countervailing forces which might check the tendency to rising costs and make the health care system more responsive to consumer preferences.

C. HOW TO CHECK ON THE DOCTORS

The fundamental reason for the problems outlined in the previous few pages of course is that the system tends to provide the patient with inadequate information, both regarding the medical value of many of the health services he consumes, and also regarding their cost. Furthermore, under comprehensive insurance, an individual patient does not have much of an incentive to acquire better information. While it may occasionally seem a nuisance to have to pay frequent return visits to your doctor, or to have to be hospitalized 'for observation', as long as the insurance pays for it it may seem a small price to pay if one believes that the visits have *some* medical justification.

Even with insurance, the consumer pays
Indirectly, however, patients must ultimately pay the price. As health services consumption rises and the unit costs remain high, the premium level for comprehensive insurance must also rise, at least in the case of unsubsidized insurance supplied privately through the market. Thus indirectly, the cost to the patients of a system where the decisions are in effect left to the doctors, may in the end become quite high.

But in a relatively unrestricted market system, the patient doesn't *have* to have comprehensive insurance, nor does the system of paying health services providers *have* to be a straight fee-for-service system. As a consequence, it is reasonable to think that in a truly unrestricted market system, there would arise a number of ways in which contractual arrangements between patients, insurers, and health services providers, could be modified so as to check the tendencies toward ''excessive'' consumption at high cost.

Free market responses to rising health costs
First, and perhaps most importantly, many patients would try to save money for themselves by reducing the extent of their insurance coverage and taking a greater degree of financial responsibility on themselves for their health services consumption. As I argued above, this could be accomplished by buying insurance with a major deductible or with some degree of co-insurance (i.e., where the patient pays a certain fraction, say 20 per cent, of his health care costs). A patient who pays all or a major part of the cost will obviously have more of an incentive to try to find out for himself whether an additional visit to the doctor is really necessary, whether he really *has* to be hospitalized for observation (or stay an extra day in the hospital), or whether it really *would* help to have junior's tonsils removed. He will have a good deal more of an incentive to seek out a doctor who does not seem to charge high fees or who does not seem to want him to come back all the time. Conversely, a doctor who knows that the

patient pays his own bill may adopt a bit more of a conservative attitude toward diagnostic tests, for example, not just because he ultimately runs the risk of losing a patient who begins to feel that he is too inclined to recommend high-cost services, but also for ethical reasons. Reducing the extent of insurance coverage in effect tends to transfer some of the decision-making for health services consumption back to the patient, by giving him financial incentive to do so, and hence reduces the degree to which the total cost of health services simply reflects doctors' decisions.

Contractual arrangements?

Another avenue through which an unrestricted market system may create a tendency to reduce the discretionary power of physicians will be via various forms of contractual arrangements between insurance companies and health services providers. For example, an insurance company which can negotiate fees with specific doctors and hospitals (and obtain guarantees that their insured patients will not be billed in excess of these fees) will obviously have a bit of a competitive edge over companies which simply pay whatever cost that doctors and hospitals choose to charge the patients. Why would doctors or hospitals enter such agreements with the insurance companies? Perhaps because they may be guaranteed payment directly from the insurer without having to bill the patient; or perhaps because they might want to attract patients by contracting not to charge in excess of the insured rates.

Arrangements of this kind can be expected to strengthen competition both in the market for insurance and in the market for health services, and there is evidence from the U.S. that there has been strong competition between conventional health insurance and the so-called Blue Plans (Blue Cross, Blue Shield), which negotiate directly with providers regarding fee schedules.

But while these arrangements give the insurance companies some control over the price *per unit* of physician or hospital services, they do not have a direct impact on the *quantity* of services which the doctor and the patient jointly decide on. The question therefore arises whether a market-oriented system could not also include arrangements whereby insurance could be provided more cheaply by having the insuring organization exercise some control over the actual services provided, not just their cost.

Medical repair 'adjusters'?

It is interesting to observe here that in the auto insurance industry, the companies do indeed attempt to exercise control over both services and cost. When your car gets damaged in an accident, you first go to see an insurance adjuster who assesses the damage and estimates the need for repairs and the cost. He then sends you on your way to get several estimates from different repairshops, and unless there is prior agreement between yourself and the adjuster with respect to the extent of work required and the cost, there is no guarantee that your claim will be paid and you may have to take the insurer to court if you want to try to get your money.

In principle, there seems to be no reason why similar procedures could not be used, at least for some types of insured services, in the health insurance field. For some types of elective surgery, diagnostic tests, etc., the insurance contract might stipulate that you have to have the approval of a company doctor before they would guarantee reimbursement.† Again, for some types of treatment contracts of this kind might lead to substantial cost reduction. Consider for example the evidence from the Saskatchewan hysterectomy study referred to above. It is probably safe to hypothesize that the number of "medically unnecessary" cases of surgery would have been quite a bit lower if each operation had required the approval of a doctor employed by an insurance company, or even if it had been known that a number of randomly selected ones would be subject to checking by such doctors. Under present Canadian law, contracts to this effect would probably be illegal (and would certainly not be supported by the medical profession) because they would interfere with the patient's freedom to choose his own doctor and would involve a person other than the patient and his doctor in a medical decision. With different legislation, however, the method would provide one way of putting pressure on the tendency for medical costs to rise.

---

† Editor's Note: This procedure is already followed in the case of some Dental Insurance Plans: for example, the Dental Health Services Plan of British Columbia.

Prepaid group practices

The logical conclusion from this line of argument, in fact, would be to ask whether the insurance function and health services provision could not be integrated? In other words, the insurance companies could employ doctors or have their own hospitals in order to provide directly the services covered by their insurance. Equivalently, groups of doctors could get together to operate a business in which they provide specified sets of health services (perhaps including hospital services) in exchange for a fixed annual charge; this charge would be analogous to an insurance premium.

Institutions of this kind do in fact exist in some countries: the so-called prepaid group practices. Finally, there is no reason why the institutions would have to be owned and managed by doctors or insurance companies: they could be organized as independent (for profit or non-profit) enterprises which would offer prepaid plans (i.e., health insurance) consisting of a comprehensive set of health services provided by doctors employed by them and hospitals owned by the enterprise. Again, organizations of this kind do exist in the real world: as I will describe in the next chapter, in the U.S. system there exist a number of "Health Maintenance Organizations" which employ their own doctors on a salary basis, operate their own hospitals, and provide all medical treatment (with some limitations) to their subscribers in return for a fixed annual charge. In other words, the subscribers to these schemes are in effect insured by the same organization which provides their health services.

From the viewpoint of dealing with the problem of the need for expert advice in making decisions with respect to health services consumption, these kinds of arrangements represent an interesting solution. Just as in a straight fee-for-service system, the advice to the patient under prepayment plans continues to come from the same doctors who provide the services. What is drastically different, however, is the financial incentive on the providers. Under fee-for-service, it is in their interest to recommend "high-quality" treatment, even though the cost may be high. All that the provider has to worry about is patient resistance, if the patients are paying their own bills, or resistance from the insurance company, if the patients are covered by insurance. Under prepayment plans, on the other hand, the providers' interest is to provide treatment at low cost; their problem is not that of overcoming patient or insurance company resistance to high cost, but rather to provide services which are good enough to ensure that the patients retain their confidence in the plan and continue to remain in it.

The prepayment-type solution to the problem of the need for the consumer to rely on the expertise of the provider does of course exist in other markets as well. A building contractor who agrees to undertake a given project for a price specified in advance is in the same kind of situation as a doctor in a pre-paid plan. The contractor's interest lies in getting the job done as efficiently and cheaply as possible, but well enough to maintain his reputation and generate repeat business. A contractor who works on a time-and-materials basis is like a doctor under fee-for-service paid by the patient: the more of his services he sells the customer, the better off he is. Of course, if the cost goes too high, (in particular, higher than his competitors) the customer might complain or seek to break the contract. The doctor under a fee-for-service system with the payment coming from insurance is, in effect, like a contractor on a time-and-materials basis with a customer whose bills are paid by a rich uncle. Both the contractor and the customer would presumably agree that they would want "the best", with the only possible resistance coming from the uncle. In this sense, a comprehensive universal health insurance plan means that we are all each others' rich uncles, through the premiums or taxes we pay.

Given the complex nature of medicine and health care, it will obviously always remain true that to a large extent, the patient/consumer will have to make his choices with very imperfect information, and it is also inevitable that the doctors who provide the services also will remain the source for much of the information that the patient needs to make his decisions. But to argue from this that the patient has no effective room for choice, and that the market allocation of resources to the health services sector will necessarily and completely be determined by the actions of self-interested medical men, is a gross exaggeration. As I have argued, if the market system is *restricted,* so that every patient must have comprehensive health insurance and providers only can be paid on a fee-for-service basis, the incentive on individuals to make choices for themselves will have been removed, and the doctors will in effect be making most of the choices. But such a system will be expensive, and if the restrictions are lifted a competitive market would develop alternative contractual arrangements of the kind discussed in this section. These developments would, to a large extent, restore the patient's incentive to control his own health services consumption, by allowing him to choose between different types of insurance contracts (including no insurance!), between fee-for-service physicians and doctors in prepayment plans, and so on.

D. SUMMARY: CONSUMER SOVEREIGNTY AND THE DEMAND FOR HEALTH SERVICES

At this point, it will be useful to summarize the discussion in the preceding pages, in order to consider the question whether the demand for health services in a market-oriented system may be consistent with the principle of consumer sovereignty: that is, whether the demand can be said to reflect consumers' valuation of health services relative to other goods and services, as it would have to if the market were to function as an effective device to allocate resources to this sector.

Does insurance negate effective choice?
First, in a market-oriented system, most people would be covered by health insurance of some form: conventional insurance with varying degrees of comprehensiveness, or "insurance" through enrollment in some form of prepayment plan, or some combination thereof. Even though the purchase of health insurance represents only a *conditional* decision to consume health services, differences in individual valuations of various kinds of health services can still be accommodated, since the form and extent of insurance coverage is decided on by the individual himself. For example, a person who does not have a high valuation of health services when suffering from minor ailments can buy low-cost insurance with a relatively high deductible; conversely, an individual who values them highly even for treatment of minor ailments will buy comprehensive first-dollar coverage at a higher cost. Hence, one can argue that the possibility of varying the extent of insurance coverage makes

it possible for the consumer to vary his *expected* demand for health services in accordance with his willingness to pay for them. The existence of insurance per se does not negate this principle.

The crucial role of information
The more serious objection against the principle of consumer sovereignty is based on the problem of insufficient consumer information about the effectiveness of the health services they consume or insure themselves against. In a situation where the consumer's information regarding the value of health services is supplied by the providers of medical care, who, after all, stand to gain from an increase in the demand for their services, what guarantee is there that the information supplied will not become increasingly misleading and that the level of services provided will not be far in excess of the consumer's willingness to pay for them if he had better information? The answer to this question lies in the profitability of providing better information: in general, if consumers are paying a high price for a product because they mistakenly believe that it is superior to a low-priced one, it will become profitable to supply them with better information and to market the lower-priced one. A good example is the increasing competition that high-priced brand-name drugs (e.g., aspirin) are now getting from the lower-priced "generic" drugs. In the health services field, one can argue that HMOs or other forms of prepayment plans might be playing the role of generic aspirin: if many people come to believe that their services do about as much for their health as does conventional medicine, but without the expensive frills, competition from HMOs will provide a powerful check on the rising cost of conventional medicine.[12]

Risk and preventive measures
To a considerable extent, therefore, the market mechanism would provide the consumer with choices about health services so that he can vary the amount he expects to consume according to his willingness to pay. Furthermore, as noted above, the market system may to some extent provide incentives for people to substitute other means than health services in attaining good health. For example, if competition between insurers produces discrimination between risk classes, and individuals could

influence their own risk rating by not smoking, keeping fit, and so on, they can save themselves money on insurance premia (or save their own money, if they have contracts with deductibles), and save society resources, by reducing the expected amounts of health services consumed. At least in a rough sense, one may thus argue that the amount of money that individuals are willing to pay for health services would reflect the value they attach to them relative to other goods and services.

V. THE SUPPLY SIDE

A. THE MEANING OF COMPETITIVE SUPPLY

The opportunity cost of health care

In a market system, when the consumer decides how much money to spend on a particular good such as health services, he is indirectly deciding how much to give up of other things. As has been discussed before, the information that the consumer uses in making these choices consists of prices: whether he wants to spend more or less on health services at a particular time depends on the price of health services relative to other things.

But it should be clear that in a system of resource allocation which is supposed to serve the interests of consumers, (i.e., in order for consumer choices to be made efficiently) prices must correctly reflect the real cost, or the *opportunity* cost, of producing things: if society wants more of something, how much of other things have to be given up? Thus, the price of health services should tell consumers how much housing, or automobiles, or haircuts, have to be given up in order to produce a specified amount of additional health services. It should also be obvious that in an efficient system, a given amount of health services should be produced as *cheaply* as possible, i.e., with a minimum amount of resources, so that as little as possible of other things is sacrificed if a specific amount of health services are to be produced.

Whose interest is served?

In general, it is of course not in the self-interest of producers to behave according to these requirements. Other things equal, a producer is interested in selling his goods at the most profitable price, not the lowest. Neither is it always in the best interest of those participating in the production process that the most efficient (i.e., lowest-cost) production method be used: the most typical case is perhaps when the lowest-cost method is a mechanized one whose introduction would involve a loss of jobs. The producing firms may favour it, but the industry union will not.

Competition the key
The way in which the efficiency requirements are reconciled with the self-interest of producers and resource owners is through competition between firms motivated by the search for profits. If there are no restrictions on the methods of production, the most efficient firms will be making the highest profits. If there are no restrictions on capacity expansion by existing firms, or on entry into the industry by new firms, high profits will lead to expanded production capacity and an increase in quantity supplied to the market. If there are no restrictions, finally, on price setting, the increased supply can only be sold in the market at lower prices. This will tend to reduce profits, and in the economist's competitive equilibrium, the price is just high enough to cover the cost of production when the most efficient technology is used, and profits are just high enough to prevent existing firms from leaving the industry but not high enough to attract new firms.

Does it work?
The question to be addressed in this section is to what extent the health services industry is likely to fit this picture under a market-oriented system. For example, is there effective competition between doctors, so that an increase in the amount of physician services leads to lower fees, and will high physician incomes lead to an expansion in the quantity of services offered? Is there competitive pressure on hospitals, so that new and efficient technologies are continuously introduced, reducing the effective cost of hospital services? And so on.

B. INTERDEPENDENT SUPPLY AND DEMAND ONCE AGAIN

As discussed at length in an earlier section, many people have argued that the traditional model of a "market", in which consumers are making their own decisions how much to buy on the basis of market prices alone, does not fit the health services industry because to a substantial extent the "consumption" decisions are influenced, if not entirely controlled, by the doctors. Clearly, from the consumers' viewpoint, such a situation is undesirable because it means that their interest in having health services contribute to their good health, at reasonable cost, is no longer the only criterion according to which choices are made. Instead, the choices may more and more come to reflect the interests and objectives of the health services providers.

Lack of effective competition

From the present perspective, the significant point to note is that the possibility of "demand generation" by doctors arises because there is little effective competition between them. In part, the reason why competitive forces may be weak is simply the patient's difficulty in evaluating the effectiveness of different types of medical services in contributing to his health. Under these circumstances, it is difficult for a patient to distinguish between a doctor who provides a good health services package at low cost because he is efficient, and one who sacrifices "quality" in order to keep costs down. In other words, a doctor attempting to compete by reducing price may be classified as "cheap" in the sense that the quality of the services he provides is suspect. Similar problems may arise if the doctor tries to be efficient in the way he produces his services. For example, he may delegate some routine procedures (tests, inoculations, etc.) to his nurse or paramedical assistant, or he may attempt to dissuade his patients from making office visits if they have vague or non-specific symptoms. These practices may be perfectly acceptable as far as the risks to the patient's health are concerned, but to the patients they may give the impression that the doctor is not taking them seriously and they may look for another one. Again, the medical profession is not alone in facing this problem: similar considerations apply to lawyers, for example.

When the patient pays for his own services, a strategy of "judging quality by price" will be expensive, however. Particularly if fee schedules are widely publicized so that it is readily apparent which doctors are high-priced and which ones are not, doctors who both provide good service and who are reasonably priced, will quickly become known. Even though patients may be reluctant to switch family doctors, say, at the drop of a hat, if price differences become wide enough they will. New doctors trying to establish themselves in practice have no reputation to fall back on, and their only means of building up a practice will be to offer service at relatively low fees. For these reasons, unless there are outright restrictions on pricing or fee publication, in a market where the patient pays directly, one could perhaps expect price competition to work reasonably well.

Insurance blunts the patient's economy concerns

When patients are covered by comprehensive, open-ended health insurance, on the other hand, the situation changes drastically. If the insurance pays for the services of any doctor, the patient has no direct incentive to seek out doctors who provide low-cost health service packages. The incentive on the patient is to seek out the highest-quality care regardless of cost. Therefore, the incentive on the doctor who wants to retain his patients is to *provide* the highest possible quality of care, regardless of cost. Thus the fundamental problem in this kind of situation is that the institutional form of the market for physician services is such that there is little pressure on doctors to compete via price. A high-priced barber will lose his customers; a high-priced doctor will not. A barber who invents a new and cheaper way of cutting hair can always attract as many customers as he wants by reducing his price; an efficient doctor cannot. Other things equal, an economist would predict that in such a market, the pace of technological progress would be slow, and the commodity sold would sometimes be inefficiently produced, and would in any case be high-priced. If in addition, the producer can to a substantial extent control the demand for his individual product, the economist would also predict that producer incomes would be high, and there would be a steady tendency for new producers to enter the market. A look at the application rates to Canadian or U.S. medical schools certainly supports this part of the prediction!

Hospitals also affected

The picture is somewhat similar in the market for hospital services. If all potential patients have comprehensive insurance coverage without limitation, the choice of hospital (or the decision whether or not to hospitalize) made by the patient and his doctor is unaffected by cost considerations, and competition for patients and doctors to use the hospital would then manifest itself in attempts at raising the quality of service. To appeal to patients, one may offer semi-private accommodation rather than public wards, and offer high-quality "hotel services" such as room telephones, televisions, and good food. The doctors may like hospitals with a wide range of specialized equipment such as intensive-care units, cardiac units or extensive radiology equipment, and the hospital may acquire them even if utilization rates are likely to be low. The pressure to produce efficiently, i.e., at low cost, is not likely to be particularly strong. For some types of services, there may not be much choice: if the hospital wants to be able to treat patients requiring heart surgery, or radiation therapy against cancer, it has to have certain specialized facilities, and there is no choice in the matter. Nevertheless, there do exist a variety of ancillary services which can be regarded as inputs into the provision of the final medical services to be produced: laundry; laboratory services; purchasing of supplies; food services. The hospital may have a choice between producing these ancillary services itself, or buying them from the outside (perhaps from other larger hospitals). If cost considerations are not important because of widespread comprehensive insurance and lack of competition for patients, the managers have little incentive to procure these services in the cheapest way, and may prefer to have a "self-contained" hospital which has its own laboratory, say, rather than rely on outside services. Recent theoretical work on the behavior of non-profit institutions, particularly hospitals, has suggested that managers of such institutions, may have goals of their own which conflict with "efficiency", and in a situation where competitive pressures are weak, they have considerable freedom to pursue those goals.[13] Hence, there are some grounds for expecting that in such a system, hospital services may not be produced in the most efficient way, and an excessively high level of "quality" will be provided, just as I argued for the case of physician services.

Again, the problem in this situation is that hospitals are not forced to compete by price. An economist's prediction for this type of market would be similar to that for physician services: little emphasis on cost-reducing technological progress, inefficiency in some cases, and high-priced services. In addition, the lack of price competition might lead to a tendency for many new hospitals to be built since, with little price competition, a hospital can compete through location: other things equal, patients probably prefer to be hospitalized closer to home. The result might be a large number of inefficient small hospitals.

C. RE-ESTABLISHING COMPETITION:
ALTERNATIVE FORMS OF INSURANCE

Market function not appealing
The general picture which emerges from the preceding discussion of the supply of health care in a market-oriented system is not an appealing one. The prediction is that under widespread comprehensive health insurance and independent fee-for-service providers of health services, competition between providers would be weak. The result would be numerous small-scale and inefficient hospitals oversupplied with sophisticated equipment, large numbers of doctors with a relatively small number of patients, busily generating demand for their own services and those of the hospitals by advising patients to undergo all sorts of tests and treatments without regard for cost and of doubtful medical value. Costs would be high, and there would be a constant tendency for more doctors to enter practice, generating more demand and higher total expenditure; new hospitals would be built to meet the "generated" demand for their services.

It is worth noting in this context that the implicit notion of doctors being able to generate the demand for their own and the hospitals' services has figured prominently in recent political discussion of health services in Canada. Thus, Frank Miller (at the time the Ontario Minister of Health) recently suggested that the way to reduce the growth rate of health care costs was to reduce the growth in the number of doctors. This suggestion was based on an estimate that each doctor "generates" health care costs (including hospitalization) of 200-250 thousand dollars per annum, and that each additional doctor would, directly and indirectly, add this amount to total cost.[14] The logic implied in this argument must be that health care costs are independent of the number of patients to be treated, and is primarily determined by the number of doctors. It is difficult to justify this reasoning unless one believes that doctors are able to control the demand for health care services more or less at will.

Health Maintenance Organizations—breaking the cost spiral
The preceding discussion of the supply side in a market system is based on the assumption that the system would operate on a fee-for-service basis, however, and that conventional comprehensive health insurance would be widespread, as it is in Canada. As I discussed in some detail above, if patients have to pay directly for their own health insurance, high and rising cost would make it increasingly profitable to offer alternative forms of health insurance at lower cost if this were permitted. Suppose we consider a situation where health costs are high, comprehensive insurance is widespread, and providers are paid on a fee-for-service basis, and suppose that prepayment plans such as HMOs begin to compete with conventional insurance. If it is indeed true that HMOs are able to offer equivalent comprehensive care at lower cost, it would follow that at this stage, they would be very profitable operations. Under those circumstances, existing HMOs would have an incentive to expand their facilities, and one would expect more of them to be started. Unless this process were to be slowed down through various forms of restrictions against entry of new plans, the resulting increase in the supply of HMO services would then lead to increasing competition for new subscribers. To some extent, competition might take the form of offering higher "quality" of service, rather than lower price, in the same way as was described above for the case of doctors and hospitals under a fee-for-service system. But the point is that the incentives on an HMO to compete through "price" (i.e., subscription rates) are much stronger than they would be under a fee-for-service system with conventional insurance. As argued above, under the latter system, *nobody* (insurers or providers) has an incentive to compete by price. When the insurance and provision functions are integrated, however, as they are in HMOs, this is not so: they are equivalent to insurance companies

who can control the efficiency and cost of the medical services against which they insure their subscribers, since they themselves do the providing.

If HMOs are growing, conventional insurance must be losing customers, and fee-for-service providers must be seeing their patient numbers decline. One likely consequence of this would be increasing attempts by insurance companies to compete by offering lower-cost policies with deductibles, co-insurance provisions, and various other limitations, as also discussed above. Deductibles and co-insurance provisions, in turn, would make individual patients more sensitive to the fees of doctors and hospitals, so that this might tend to intensify price competition between providers as well.

Lack of competition is not an inherent characteristic of health industry

The argument with which I started this section was the one stating that "the market won't work" on the supply side for the health services sector, because providers control the demand for their own services. From the present perspective, it becomes clear that this is really an argument about the effectiveness of competition: it is believed that the model of a competitive market is inapplicable because health services providers do not compete for business through the price of their services.

The conclusion from the discussion is that the absence of effective price competition is not an inherent characteristic of the market for health services. Rather, the absence of competition in a system such as the Canadian one, for example, has arisen because of the introduction of universal comprehensive and open-ended health insurance in combination with a fee-for-service system to pay the providers of health services. Such a system entirely eliminates the *incentive* to compete. In an unrestricted market, however, in which individuals had freedom to choose the form of their insurance coverage for themselves, and in which providers were free to offer services in other ways than on a fee-for-service basis, competitive forces would reassert themselves. The result might be a system of health services provisions that would reasonably well conform to the economist's ideal: efficient production at the lowest possible cost, with the amounts produced being determined in a flexible way according to the preferences of the *consumers* of health services, not according to the interests of the providers.

Elimination of the present institutional barriers to competition, however, is only a necessary condition for an efficient market. In any market, there will be groups opposed to competition because it is contrary to their economic interests, and in general, attempts to remove one set of barriers to competition through changes in legislation will be met by efforts by such groups to establish new ones through other measures. In the health services field, the most important interest group is "organized medicine"; in the next section I turn to a discussion of the ways in which it may act to protect its members' interests.

D. ACTIVITIES OF ORGANIZED MEDICINE TO PREVENT COMPETITION

'A conspiracy against the public'?

It was argued above that, rhetorical statements at business conventions notwithstanding, most firms in any industry would prefer competition to be less intense rather than more intense: more competition means lower prices and profits, more pressure on firms using obsolete and high-cost technology, and so on. While this all benefits consumers, most businessmen probably would prefer for themselves a bit more of the "quiet (and profitable) life of the monopolist" as economists sometimes describe a situation in which competition has been eliminated or restricted in one way or another. Adam Smith put it this way in 1776: "People of the same trade seldom meet together, even for merriment and diversion, but the conversation ends in a conspiracy against the public, or in some contrivance to raise prices."[15] There are many people who believe that this description may not be totally inappropriate as a characterization of the annual meeting of a professional association of medical practitioners, say.

Like all such associations, the medical ones have conflicting objectives.[16] On the one hand, they are there to protect the interests of the public by ensuring that their members refrain from practices that may be profitable for the individual professional but harmful to the consumer. On the other hand, professional associations are also there in order to protect the interests of their members. If the medical association wants to "protect the public against unscrupulous practices", it also wants to make sure that doctors get "adequate pay for a good day's work". If competition between doctors for patients is too intense, the result may be falling fees for medical services and declining incomes of doctors, which may be seen as inconsistent with that objective.

As I argued above, with the advent of widespread comprehensive health insurance, the incentive for individual fee-for-service physicians to engage in price competition has been greatly reduced, and the activities of organized medicine to regulate competition among its members are not as prominent as they once were. The evidence from an earlier era when most patients paid for physician services out of their own pockets, however, provides interesting examples of actions of organized medicine which were effective in reducing the extent of price competition. The evidence also illustrates how in many cases such measures could be "sold" to the public by appealing to the legitimate concern for the "quality" of medical practice.

Informal welfarism—price discrimination by doctors
It is well known that at one time the principle of charging for physician services according to the patient's income was widely practiced among North American doctors. The principle is easy to justify: the doctors' claim was that it represented a scheme whereby subsidized medical care could be provided to low-income patients, with the subsidy in effect coming from the well-to-do ones.

In the terminology of economics, a situation in which different buyers are charged different prices for the same good or service, is called price discrimination. While it is obviously true that price discrimination according to the consumer's income relatively favours low-income people, it is also true that if properly carried out, it represents a way for the producer to extract a higher revenue from a given group of customers. Whether discriminatory pricing for physician services was in fact undertaken primarily for the benefit of the low-income patients or for the benefit of the doctors who practised it, is not the relevant point here: it is indeed likely that if it had not in fact existed, the result would have been higher cost of health care for the low-income group. But it is also true that had it not existed the level of physician income would have been lower.

Enforcing price discrimination—
the 'unethics' of advertising

The question of primary interest here, however, concerns the methods by which adherence to the system was maintained. For it to work effectively, it is clearly necessary for doctors to refrain from competing with each other for the lucrative high-income patients: while "comparison shopping" may sometimes be difficult, for example when a patient suffers from an ill-defined or imperfectly diagnosed ailment, there does exist a wide range of fairly standard medical procedures for which patients can compare fees between doctors. If publication of fee schedules for such procedures were permitted, a doctor offering to perform them at prices somewhat below the prevailing fees for high-income patients would attract large numbers of such patients away from those doctors who continued to practice discriminatory pricing. In the end, the pricing system would tend to break down and a more or less uniform fee schedule would come to prevail.

Now medical associations (like the legal ones) have long maintained a tradition that the publication of physician fee schedules constitutes "unethical" practice. The justification has been that the public needs to be protected against "cut-rate medicine", i.e., against the substandard medical practice that might result if ill-informed consumers were to be too intent on looking for the lowest-cost package of services. At the same time, of course, a ban on advertising also effectively eliminated the opportunity for doctors to compete for patients by publicizing a fixed fee schedule, as just discussed. Thus, restrictions on advertising may conceivably be in the patient's interest, as a protection against unscrupulous doctors. But they also represent a necessary ingredient in a discriminatory pricing system which may be designed to raise physician incomes: it protects the doctor against the greedy patient, as it were.

**The doctors versus the prepayment plan—
maintaining ethics by whatever means necessary**

As I argued above, an effective way of stimulating competition in the health services market is to allow the existence of prepayment plans as a method of paying the providers, in addition to the fee-for-service system. In his classic article on the efforts of organized medicine to restrict competition, Reuben Kessel has carefully documented the remarkably vigorous opposition that was mounted against attempts at organizing such plans in the U.S.[17] A prepayment plan, of course, cannot practice discriminatory pricing and in order to attract patients it has to publicize its existence and its prepayment charges. In a number of cases, doctors who attempted to organize or work for such plans were informed that those practices constituted violations against the no-advertising rule. These attitudes certainly did not encourage the formation of prepayment plans. As Kessel notes, the medical profession has traditionally maintained a particularly strong *esprit de corps,* with doctors being reluctant to criticize each other before outsiders, traditionally providing treatment for each other without charge, etc. The force of moral suasion can be expected to be especially strong in such a group.

Against those who did not respond to the moral pressure to maintain those "ethical standards", stronger measures were sometimes used. A powerful device was the threat of exclusion from the local medical association. Because those associations typically had exclusive agreements with the local hospitals, this would generally mean loss of hospital privileges, i.e., the doctor excluded from the association would not be able to treat his patients in local hospitals. This of course made it very difficult for such doctors to earn a living in the practice of medicine.

**Keep out the substitutes—
protect the patient from paramedics**

Like other interest groups, organized medicine also concerns itself with the problem of competition from outside groups which provide the same or very similar services. In the medical field, this largely relates to the role of paramedical personnel in providing health services: the attitude of organized medicine toward permitting paramedical personnel to perform some of the functions presently done by physicians, has always been conservative. The ostensible motive has been to protect the patient against faulty diagnosis or treatment by insufficiently qualified personnel; but again, it is difficult to believe that a concern for the demand for the services of doctors and hence their potential income, has not been an important motive as well. Consider for example the following newspaper account[18] of an address by Dr. Robert Gourdeau, outgoing president of the Canadian Medical Association:

"It's time Canadian doctors did something to end the 'continuous and systematic erosion' of their territory by a horde of other allied health workers, the president of the Canadian Medical Association (CMA) warned here Wednesday.

Dr. Robert Gourdeau of Quebec City said that for many years an increasing number of paramedical bodies—for reasons of ambition, prestige, autonomy, economics and other professional or personal reasons, not always related to the common good of the public—have been pressuring to increase their responsibility. He told a CMA gathering that doctors could face a 'painful tomorrow if we do not give this problem the time and energy necessary to develop appropriate means toward this invasion.' He said medicine must ensure that those who practise the profession are appropriately trained and licensed to do so. He cited the case of Ontario psychologists who have proposed a new definition for their profession; 'Professional responsibilities and authority that is tantamount to the definition of psychiatry.' These people, he said, are asking the exclusive right to treat their clients according to the new definition of psychology.

There were others he said including podiatrists, a form of non-doctor foot specialist, who in some cases are practising what he feels is major surgery. Even nurses are asking for authority to perform numerous medical acts, sometimes with the support of doctors. Gourdeau warned that the requests of such groups often fall on 'fertile soil' because governments, for reasons of political expediency or attempts to cut health costs, are tempted to go along with them. 'The financial savings often prove illusory and the quality of medical care is jeopardized,' he said. He called on doctors to educate their patients 'to confound those who strive to expropriate, for their own profit, a greater share of our domain....' ''

To me, at least, this represents a very thinly veiled statement of the medical profession's determination to protect their economic interests by resisting competition from outsiders.

Limiting entry—control over the supply of new doctors

Apart from the competition between existing firms or individuals in an industry, there is furthermore always the threat of potential competition from new entrants to the industry. If plumbing becomes a profitable occupation, more people will want to transfer from other occupations and establish themselves in the plumbing business; if doctors' incomes are high, more people will want to go through medical schools and become doctors. Indeed, the greater the success of existing firms in an industry in limiting competition among themselves, the greater is the threat of new entry into the industry. Hence, the strategy of an effort to safeguard the economic interests of the firms or individuals in an industry (or, for that matter, in a particular segment of the labour market) by limiting competition, is nearly always two-pronged. On the one hand, it attempts to restrict the intensity of competition within the existing industry; on the other hand, it must also attempt to control and restrict the entry of new firms into the market.

Again it is interesting to consider the activities of the interest groups in the health services field in this respect. Perhaps the most frequently discussed example are the efforts of the medical associations to exercise some degree of control over the supply of physicians, through their power to set licensing requirements for entry into medical practice.

The common justification for a physician licensing system is that there is a need to protect the patient. Since it is difficult for a layman to distinguish between a good and a bad doctor (i.e., to assess the quality of his training and hence to predict the quality of the services he will render), it seems a good idea to have some means to give assurance to patients that anybody trained as a doctor (or for that matter, as a nurse, or physiotherapist or druggist) possesses certain well-defined qualifications. The quality control functions can be carried out in many ways: by setting qualifying examinations for immigrant physicians; by reserving the possibility of barring a doctor from practising medicine in cases of malpractice, and so on. But by far their most important lever consists of their direct or indirect powers to regulate the required standards in medical training.

In the U.S. system, the role of the A.M.A. in this respect is quite unambiguous: a university proposing to open a medical school requires accreditation from the A.M.A. before its graduates will be permitted to practice medicine. In Canada, the influence of the medical associations appear less strong in this regard; the opening of a medical school depends on decisions made by provincial ministries of education. But in Canada, too, the medical associations have the final say with regard to the qualifications necessary to practice medicine, and it is difficult to imagine that substantial expansion of the capacity to train new physicians could take place, without at least a good deal of negotiation and consultation with those organizations.

Thus, through their responsibility for quality control, the medical associations do in fact indirectly have some degree of control over entry into the medical field. But again this power does create a potential conflict of interest: the ability to restrict entry for the purpose of maintaining high quality standards can be used for the purpose of protecting the incomes of doctors as well. If an increased number of doctors leads to lower incomes for existing ones, a policy of refusing accreditation to new medical schools will clearly be in the interest of existing doctors, regardless of the quality of the proposed programs. Thus, the efforts of organized medicine in this area can also be seen simply as the second part of a two-pronged strategy to limit competition and protect doctors' incomes, as discussed above.

Quality control versus income protection

For an outsider, it is again difficult to assess the relative importance of the quality-control and the income-protection motives in existing regulation of medical practice in North America. It has often been recognized that the problem of sufficient formal qualifications for medical practice may sometimes be fairly serious for older doctors who have been out of medical school for a long time, and who have not taken the trouble to keep up with changes in medical technology. If that indeed were the case, one would expect that the medical associations should be as concerned with checking the qualifications of existing practitioners (for example, through periodical examinations) as they are with those of recent graduates. In practice, this does not seem to have been the case, which again is consistent with the idea that the income protection motive does play a major role in this context.

Does organized medicine make reliance on the market impossible?

The implication of the discussion in this section may be seen as somewhat discouraging. What is being suggested is that even if one removes various institutional obstacles which at present tend to inhibit competition in the market for health services in Canada (such as universal comprehensive insurance, legislation against restricting the patient's choice of doctor, etc.), this may not be sufficient to establish a competitive market. Instead, it may simply give rise to various countermeasures by organized medicine, in the form of internal codes of conducts, or even successful lobbying for other forms of legislation, which again would eliminate or restrict competition. Doesn't this invalidate the arguments of those who favour reliance on "the automatic forces of supply and demand"?

The answer hinges to a considerable extent on what one means by "automatic". The most extreme group of market advocates, those who believe in the so-called "laissez-faire" principle, essentially argue against any kind of legislative interference in the competitive process. In their eyes unrestricted competition will "automatically" bring about a pattern of resource allocation that more or less corresponds to the public interest, or at least is better than any allocation which is likely to result from public intervention. This group, however, is in a minority. A much larger group of economists favours reliance on the market mechanism as an *instrument*, to be used in conjunction with legislative restriction when appropriate, to bring about such an allocation. To this group, there is nothing inherently wrong with legislation to protect the public against inadequately trained doctors, for example. But they also recognize the need for legislation designed to *strengthen* competition, and the need for political action to resist the pressure of lobbies who are attempting to obtain legislation in their own rather than the public's interest. Vigorously enforced anti-combines legislation is an example of the former; resistance against legislation requiring denturists to be supervised by dentists, of the latter.

Most economists who support the market, therefore, recognize that if the "automatic forces of supply and demand" are to function as intended, they have to be continuously protected by political action. To them, therefore, the choice is not between "socialized medicine" or laissez-faire. Instead, they contend that it is possible to design supporting legislation so as to *make* the market mechanism function as an efficient mechanism for resource allocation; legislation controlling the power and circumscribing the activities of organized medicine of the kind discussed in this section is an example of this.

E. SUMMARY: CHARACTERISTICS OF AN EFFICIENT MARKET FOR HEALTH SERVICES

I now turn to a brief summary of the operation of a somewhat idealized picture of a market-oriented health services system that emerges from the preceding discussion.

A differentiated health insurance system

First, it would have a differentiated health insurance system: there would be conventional insurance policies with different rates depending on risk class (so that the consumer would have some incentive to influence his own risk rating in various ways), and with different rates depending on coinsurance and deductibility provisions. There would also be non-conventional health insurance in the form of prepaid plans, so that the consumer would have the choice between higher-cost alternatives under which he can choose his own fee-for-service doctor (conventional insurance) or lower-cost ones under which he is insured against services provided by the plan doctors who work for a salary (prepayment plans). Competition between these various forms of insurance and services provision would ensure that the

price of health insurance would reflect the consumer's willingness to pay for them, with little possibility of "demand
creation". If fee-for-service physicians and hospitals were to try
to supply services in excess of what they were "worth" to the
patient, the price of conventional health insurance would rise and
people would switch to prepaid plans. To maintain competitive
rates, fee-for-service and group-plan hospitals would have an
incentive to produce their services as efficiently as possible, i.e.,
as cheaply as possible.

Few restrictions on new doctors or new hospitals

Second, a well-functioning health services system based on the
market mechanism would have few restrictions on the establish-
ment of new hospitals, or on the entry of new doctors into the
system. In particular, anybody who wanted to undergo training to
become a doctor should be allowed to do so, and if this were to
require an expansion of the medical school system, there should
be no barriers against such expansion. Similar considerations
apply to the training of para-professional medical personnel.
While there would obviously have to be some mechanism to deal
with inferior training programs or unqualified individual
practitioners, this mechanism should be as independent as
possible of the medical associations and other interest groups
representing existing providers. Under these conditions, a high
"price" of medical services would then cause resources to flow
into this sector (new hospitals would be started, more doctors and
para-professionals would be trained and enter the system), and
the increased "quantity" of health services would cause the
"price" to fall. In equilibrium, the "price" would tend to reflect
the value of the resources used to produce health services in their
best alternative use, i.e., it would reflect the "opportunity cost"
of the resources in terms of the goods and services they could
otherwise have produced. In the light of this information on the
real cost of health services, consumers can then in effect decide
on the amount of resources they want to have allocated to health
services rather than to other things. If we believe that the
allocation of resources should be such as to reflect the consumer's
best (and, one hopes, well-informed) judgement of what is good
for him, this is precisely how we would *like* resources to be

allocated, in the market for health services as well as in that for haircuts.

VI. THE MARKET AND EQUITY

A. "EVEN IF IT DOES WORK THAT WAY, IT ISN'T FAIR"

The purpose of the preceding discussion has been to outline the way in which a reasonably well-functioning market-oriented health services system would work. Its principal advantage, I argued, was that it would create a tendency to efficient, low-cost production of health services, and would produce them in quantities that would roughly correspond to individuals' preferences for health services relative to other things. In the economist's terminology, these conditions describe an *efficient* market.

During the course of the discussion, I have referred several times to skeptical views, of the "It Doesn't Work That Way" variety. Critics argue that problems such as imperfect patient information, or activities of organized medicine, or lack of competition in the insurance industry, will make reality depart so grossly from the competitive ideal that the "efficiency" advantages of the market are largely illusory. It will by now be obvious to the reader that I do not share this view.

The problem of unequal access

There is, however, a second type of criticism of the market system to which I have not yet referred extensively, namely criticism of the "Even If It Does Work That Way, It Isn't Fair" variety. Looking at the history of health services reform in various countries, it is clear that the main motivation for moving away from a system based on the individual's *willingness* to pay for them has been that under such a system, those who can *afford* to pay more will get more services. This is sometimes described as the problem of "unequal access to health care", or as a problem of different standards of medical care for rich and poor. As criticisms of the market system, all are of the general kind noted above: "Even If It Does Work That Way, It Isn't Fair".

Before discussing the implications for the health services

system in particular, it is worth pointing out that this motive of course is of broader relevance. It is in fact central to the question whether the market mechanism in general provides an acceptable method of allocating resources or whether it should be replaced by some alternative method which is more "just" and "equitable". The problem is that if the market mechanism is left on its own entirely (the "laissez-faire" principle), it will determine not only the prices of the goods and services which people consume, but also the prices of the factors of production that people sell to earn their income, i.e., the wages of different kinds of labour and the returns to the various kinds of capital assets which individuals own. Given the amounts of different factors of production (including labour) which individuals own, it will therefore indirectly determine the distribution of income between them.

But in a laissez-faire system, individual ownership of factors of production would to a large extent be a matter of sheer luck. If you are lucky, you will have been born healthy, you will have a lot of natural ability which enables you to sell your labour at a high price (as a professional hockey player or a pop singer) and which may also enable you to invest in advanced education and hence raise your future earnings (by becoming a doctor or a lawyer, say). Or you may have been lucky in the sense of being born into a home environment where as a child you receive the right kind of stimulation and guidance to accomplish these things later in life. Or, finally, you may be lucky enough to be born of rich parents whose wealth you inherit. On the other hand, you may have been born into a life of poor health, limited natural ability, a broken home, and with the old man leaving you a mortgage rather than an inheritance. Obviously, a system where individual income and welfare would be so much a matter of chance could not by any stretch of the imagination be called 'just' or 'equitable'.

The market and the 'just society'
The fact that a laissez-faire market system is not a just one, however, does not necessarily mean that the market mechanism has to be abandoned entirely if one wants a 'just' society. As anybody who has filled out an income tax return or cashed a welfare check will know, the compromise solution adopted by

Western industrial states has been to largely continue to rely on the market mechanism for the allocation of economic resources between different uses, but to mitigate its effects on the distribution of income by various forms of tax and transfer policies. Whether or not the resulting compromise represents an acceptable combination of efficiency and justice of course is one of the great issues of our time, but not one which will be considered here. Instead I will ask a more limited question which is of relevance to health care policy, namely: given that a society wishes to raise the welfare of those who otherwise would be unacceptably poor, should this be accomplished primarily by transferring *specific* goods and services which low-income families "need" (such as health care or housing), or mainly by unrestricted transfers of income, letting the recipients decide for themselves what they need?

In general, to people who subscribe to an individualistic view of the world, the latter alternative seems more rational. Suppose transfers to low-income families take the form of free housing, and consider a family whose most urgent priorities are to provide more education, or food, for its children. Such a family would be better off with an equivalent cash grant which would enable it to spend more money on education and food, but consume less housing.[19] Since different low-income families have different priorities, trying to construct an efficient welfare system based on transfers in kind would be a hopeless, or at least immensely costly, task: but a system based on transfers of income in the form of cash grants would automatically be efficient in this sense.

Welfare in kind or cash?
Can this principle be applied to health care services as well? The answer is not obvious. On the one hand, one could argue as follows. If we decide how much income to transfer to low-income families, they will decide how much health insurance they want to buy, given its price. If instead we transfer health insurance in kind (i.e., provide uniform tax financed health insurance for everybody) there would be some low-income families (e.g., those who were willing to bear a substantial amount of risk, or who did not expect to become sick) who would consider themselves better off with the equivalent cash grant and

they would buy less comprehensive health insurance if they were given cash. Based on this argument, it would be more efficient to transfer cash to low-income families and let them decide on health insurance purchases for themselves.

On the other hand, suppose we have decided, through the political mechanism, on an income tax-transfer mechanism which reflects our collective judgment regarding what is an acceptable distribution of income, and suppose that those at the low-income end would choose to buy a relatively small amount of health insurance coverage. At any given time, one would then expect there to exist a particularly unfortunate group in the society, i.e., poor people with inadequate insurance coverage who had had the bad luck to get sick. From the point of view of society as a whole, the low level of welfare in this group might then appear unacceptable, just as the low level of welfare of, say, people who are unemployed may seem unacceptable and has led to the introduction of compulsory unemployment insurance in many countries. Under those circumstances, a case can be made for the proposition that income transfer programs should in fact exist specifically for those low-income people who are seriously ill.

This need not in principle mean that health services should be transferred in kind to such individuals: the objective, presumably, is to ease the burden on the sick person in the best way that is possible, and that might mean giving him the choice between spending his income transfer on health services or on something else. In practice, however, the variability of the cost of treating serious illness and other reasons would make it difficult to design a pure income-transfer scheme that would cover all types of illness and treatment, and it may instead simply be decided to ensure that necessary treatment should be available free of direct charge to seriously ill people.

While it might be interesting to pursue further the question of the philosophical foundations for these opposing views, I do not propose to do so here. Instead I will simply assume that the second view is in fact widely accepted in modern societies, and consider a question of more interest in the present context, namely whether a market-oriented health services system is compatible with it.

B. CAN A MARKET-ORIENTED SYSTEM
BE MADE EQUITABLE?

The fundamental issue which a society must face when choosing its health care system is whether it is possible to retain the efficiency advantages of a well-functioning market-oriented system while at the same time ensuring that low-income individuals have adequate protection against financial disaster because of illness, and are not denied what society considers minimally "adequate" care. As I interpret the evidence, the increasing trend in many countries away from reliance on the market mechanism in this field stems from an implicit belief that the question must be answered in the negative. In other words, it seems to be believed that the objective of providing decent health care to the poor can only be effectively accomplished in a substantially centralized system, or conversely, that a market-oriented system will not function efficiently when the public sector intervenes to attain this objective.

Equity does not necessarily preclude efficiency
In my opinion, these views are essentially false, and I do believe that it is possible to design specific policies which make it possible to provide adequate care for low-income people without sacrificing the potential efficiency advantages of a market-oriented system which I have outlined above. I will return to the question of precisely what these policies are in Chapter Three.

But while I believe that it is false *in general* to argue that an equitable system cannot be efficient, it may certainly be true in particular cases: it all depends on the particular way in which society attempts to provide equitable access to health care. In the U.S. and Canada, to anticipate the discussion in Chapter Two, the methods used at present are to provide tax-financed comprehensive health insurance either to specific low-income groups (such as under Medicare and Medicaid in the U.S.) or to virtually everybody (such as under the provincial health insurance plans in Canada). There are few provisions for deductibles, co-payments, etc., but in either system, limits have been put on the fees that can be charged by providers for particular services. No restrictions are placed on the patient's choice of doctor or hospital, and payment to providers under these schemes is made on a fee-for-service basis.

But as the analysis in the preceding sections should have made clear, a combination of tax-financed comprehensive health insurance and a fee-for-service system of payment is not one that is likely to render the operation of a market-oriented health services system particularly efficient. It was argued there that there would be no incentive on either doctors or patients to economize on the use of health services, or on hospitals to be efficient in services provision. Competition between providers will not result in downward pressure on fees, but rather in under-utilized physicians and hospitals or at worst, in "demand creation", i.e., overprovision of services by doctors for purposes of protecting their incomes in the face of a declining patient load. Hospitals will compete by offering the widest possible range of modern equipment, etc., etc. Therefore, a major hypothesis arising from the discussion in this chapter is that a system of *providing free or subsidized health services to large parts of the population through tax-financed comprehensive health insurance, is incompatible with a market-oriented health services system.* One of the main objectives of the look at the evidence (from Canada and the U.S.) in the next chapter is to find out whether the available evidence appears broadly consistent with this notion.

VII. IF NOT THE MARKET, WHAT THEN?

The purpose of the discussion in this chapter has been to analyze how a more or less "pure" market-oriented system of resource allocation would work in the health services industry. In this final section, I turn briefly to a consideration of principal alternatives which have been suggested or used at various times to replace the market system. While it obviously is impossible to summarize the vast literature which now exists on efficient health care planning in centralized systems (such as the U.K. one) or mixed ones (such as the Canadian), it may nevertheless be useful to consider some of the main difficulties that are likely to arise, as a background to the evidence on the comparative performance of different systems provided in the next chapter.

As I already noted in the previous section, the original impetus toward modifying or abandoning the market system is most likely to come from a concern for the "equality of access" to health care for society's low-income groups, and the introduction of universal, comprehensive, health insurance has been seen as a natural consequence of this concern. For reasons discussed earlier in this chapter, the removal of financial constraints from the patient (and his doctor) in the health care consumption decision, is likely to lead initially to a rapid expansion of consumption. Depending on the method of financing the industry, this will lead to either pressure for increased taxes (if it is financed out of general revenue) or to increasing premium levels in the public insurance scheme. If there are no effective opting-out provisions, as there wouldn't be in a universal or near-universal system, however, the two are essentially equivalent: a uniform insurance premium which everybody has to pay is essentially equivalent to a head tax.

Who will hold the purse strings?

The important point of this, in any event, is that the pressure to contain health care spending will now be transferred from the patients and their doctors, to the politicians. In other words, out of a concern for "equality of access" and imperfect consumer information, we begin by in effect leaving the spending decisions to the "experts" (or, as Robert Evans has put it, instead of holding on to the purse strings we simply drop the purse and walk away).

But if the experience of the countries who have so far gone through this process proves anything at all, it is that leaving the decisions to the experts is not a viable policy. We will inevitably find that they will want to spend too much, and it becomes clear that *somebody* has to grab hold of the purse strings. If the principle of universal and comprehensive insurance is regarded as sacrosanct, so that a transfer of even part of the financial responsibility to the consumers is regarded as unacceptable, there is no more choice: financial responsibility, and hence the authority to decide on resource allocation to health services, will be taken over by the politicians. This is the process which the U.K. went through long ago and which, in my opinion, is now going on in Canada.

But this again raises the question of the decision-makers' information. Whether or not the political decisions regarding the

58

extent of health insurance and health services consumption that individual citizens should have, given the evidence available to the political decision-makers, are going to be more in accord with the "real value" of health services than decisions made by consumers themselves, given *their* evidence, is a moot point. For example, if the public has an exaggerated view of the ability of traditional health services to prolong life and ensure good health, would that not be likely to reflect itself in public pressure on elected representatives to maintain a high level of spending on health services? And while everybody may well be in favour of lower public spending and lower taxes in general, there is a marked tendency for people to prefer spending cuts by others to those affecting themselves. Thus, the government of Ontario had a good deal of support for its general policy of cutting health services spending, but attempts at implementing the policy by closing particular hospitals ran into heavy local opposition, and have been postponed for the moment. This experience raises the unpalatable possibility that rather than reflect a more "rational" allocation of health services resources than an imperfectly functioning market would accomplish, a centralized allocation may instead come to reflect the relative political clout of representatives of particular areas or interest groups.

The special interests problem
One important set of such interest groups, of course, is that consisting of the associations representing the health services producers. In fact, one of the principal difficulties with reliance on the market mechanism, according to its critics, is the political power of physicians through their professional associations: because of this power, they are seen as being able to maintain legislation which in effect eliminates competition, or block legislation which favours it. The conclusion frequently drawn from this is that any amount of attempting to tinker with the market mechanism in order to render it more efficient will founder on the opposition of, or countermeasures by, the medical profession. Thus, the only solution is seen as being the more drastic step of abandoning the market mechanism altogether in favour of a centralized system.

As far as the logic of this argument is concerned, it does raise the question why one would believe that it would be easier to deal with the power of medical associations in a centralized system. The sinister view of the associations is that they oppose competition not out of concern for patients, but because they see it as inimical to the economic self-interest of the profession. But if one takes the medical associations to have sufficient political power to block reforms which strengthen competition, why should one expect them to be less successful at protecting the interest of their members in a centralized system in which *all* decisions regarding health services provision are made through the political process? In such a system, there would have to exist a health services bureaucracy responsible for detailed decisions and for providing information and expert advice to the political decision-makers on the broader issues; this bureaucracy would necessarily have to contain medical professionals who would face the issue of divided loyalties between their fellow doctors and the public whose interests they are supposed to serve. One could argue that the professional associations would be in an even more powerful position to influence decision-making in their favour through the bureaucracy than they are in a market-oriented system where they have to exert their influence more directly on the politicians or through public opinion.

Political wrangling versus the market

The precise way in which resources would be allocated in a centralized health services system of this kind would vary from country to country, of course, and some cases will be discussed in the next chapter. In general, however, it might be characterized as a system of bureaucratic and political wrangling, with considerable resources being devoted to the study of principles of "efficient health planning". Again Canadian experience provides plenty of evidence of the sorts of things one can expect if the system moves further in a centralized direction: proposals by the government to enforce uniform hospital-bed/population ratios or physician/population ratios, met by considerable opposition from the localities and organizations involved; acrimonious bargaining regarding physician fee schedules, involving threats by doctors to opt out of public insurance schemes and counter-threats by governments to put physicians on salary; and increasingly vocal complaints by doctors of government interference with the practice of medicine for purposes of cost-cutting.

To what extent the allocation of resources resulting from this type of process closely represents the interests of those whom it is supposed to serve, the consumers/taxpayers, is not clear. What *is* clear, however, is that it doesn't make sense to compare an imperfect market mechanism with a smoothly functioning centralized system, perfectly administered by dis-interested and omniscient "experts".

The market and its critics
To sum up, the critics of the market mechanism claim that it will result in an inefficient and costly system based on restrictions of competition and exploitation of consumer ignorance for the benefit of the health services providers, to the detriment of the patients. Those who, like myself, take a more positive view of the role of the market mechanism, do not deny the existence or even the significance of these imperfections. It is obviously impossible for the average patient to acquire enough information about medicine so that he can himself decide on diagnosis and treatment, and it is unrealistic to expect that closely knit associations of professionals such as doctors should be any less inclined to serve the interests of their members by attempting to limit competition than are other interest groups. The disagreements between those for and those against the market system rather concern the *degree* to which imperfections in competition prevent the market from functioning at all (as opposed to being perfect), and the question how the system should be changed to make it more efficient. The former can only be resolved by an appeal to empirical evidence, and we will return to it in Chapter Two. The answer to the latter question depends on the specification of the alternatives. Those favouring the market mechanism will argue that the system should be improved by measures to improve consumer information and strengthen competition; Chapter Three contains a discussion of various ways in which this could be done.

Those who advocate a non-market system, on the other hand, have to concern themselves with the problem how to avoid an expensive, cumbersome, and self-serving bureaucracy in the health services sector, how to avoid the problem of having the special interest groups protecting the interests of their members through the political process (rather than through restrictions on competition), and how to avoid a situation where the allocation of health services resources come to reflect the political power of particular consumer groups rather than the ''needs'' of patients in general, (however these are to be defined). The question whether it is possible to design a reasonably well-functioning non-market system is again one which can be fully answered only in the light of empirical evidence, and it will also be considered in Chapter Two.

NOTES

[1][5], Table A1. The figure refers to fiscal 1976-77, and is a CMA estimate.

[2][33], Table III, pp. 96-97. Figures refer to 1975.

[3][24], Table 12, p. 68.

[4][5], Table E1, for 1975-76; [44], Table 1, p. 2, for 1959-60.

[5][24], Table 12, p. 68 for 1960; 1975 figure is interpolated from the 1974/75 and 1975/76 figures on total public and private health services costs from [40], Table 37, p. 56, divided by GNP given in [40], Table 344, p. 335.

[6][28], Table 1, p. 10. Ranking based on figures for "1974 or near date".

[7]See [20], especially Chapter 6, pp. 38-42.

[8][4], pp. 7-8.

[9][20], Annex A, pp. 75-76.

[9A] This view is stressed by Migué and Bélanger in [24A], Ch. 1, which contains an excellent discussion of much of the material covered in this section.

[10]See [9].

[11]See [10] and [11].

[12]For a review of studies on health care costs in HMOs see [23].

[13]See [25], [12]. In [26], the non-profit hospital is regarded as managed by the physicians who use it.

[14]Quoted in [1], p. 9.

[15][29A], Book 1, Ch. 10, Part 2, p. 103.

[16]A good general discussion of professional associations in medicine is contained in [24A], Ch. 9.

[17][17].

[18]Quoted in *The London Free Press,* Wednesday, June 21, 1978, p. A9.

[19]On this issue, see [14].

Chapter 2
THE EVIDENCE

I. INTRODUCTION: CHOICE OF CASES

The critical aspects of a health care system

From the discussion in the previous chapter, three related questions emerge as the most important ones in analyzing a system of health care financing and health services production. *First,* there is the question how the system affects the society's distribution of welfare and income. Does it or does it not result in a tendency for poor people to become sick or for sick people to become poor? These are the issues of equity and equality of access which have played such a large role historically in the public debate in most countries, and continue to do so in some. The answer clearly relates primarily to the method of financing health services consumption. As will become clear below, however, there is a good deal of evidence that the choice of financing also affects the system's efficiency in the economic sense.

Second, there are the issues of cost and quality of care. How effective is the system in producing "good health", i.e., in decreasing mortality and morbidity and in alleviating pain, suffering, and disability? Given the state of health it produces, does it do so *efficiently,* i.e., using the "best" technology and using up as little resources as possible? Or conversely, are there elements in the system that tend to cause inefficient, and costly medical technology to be used, i.e., to make the system wasteful?

Third, there is the question of the responsiveness of the system to consumers' preferences. Given that an increase in the amount of resources used in the health services sector must mean a sacrifice of other goods and services, i.e., given that health services have an *opportunity cost,* is the health services system about as big as consumers would want it? Are the right *kind* of health services being produced? Or conversely, if they were given the choice, would consumers rather see fewer health services produced and more of other things, such as housing; or is the system inefficient in the sense of providing "too little" health services; i.e., does it prevent individuals from increasing their consumption even if they were willing to pay the cost?

The evidence I will be discussing in the following sections will relate primarily to the first two questions. The reason for this is readily apparent. It is possible to get some idea of equality of access by looking at the degree of universality in the population's health insurance coverage, etc.; moreover, it is feasible to draw some conclusions about efficiency by looking at various measures of the population's health together with statistics of resource use and cost in the health care system. However, an answer to the third question is more difficult because it would require evidence on individuals' preferences, which we do not have.

But to answer the third question may be thought at least as important as to answer the first two, if one believes that freedom of choice for the individual is an important aspect of a well-functioning economic system. Hence, while the numbers I will be discussing will mostly deal with the equity-of-access and efficiency-of-production issues, I will occasionally speculate on the question whether a particular health services system really represents what individuals want for themselves, and the answer to this somewhat nebulous question is to my mind as important as the numbers in making decisions about the future directions of the Canadian health services system.

Similar societies with different health care systems

In looking for empirical evidence which would be relevant to those decisions, one would ideally like to find it from societies that are as similar to Canada as possible in other respects, but with different health services systems. Any social system, and perhaps especially the health services one with its powerful interest groups, is resistant to drastic change, and one must recognize that in the short run, most decisions must essentially refer to somewhat limited modifications of the existing system. The question then arises whether evidence derived from health care systems which are very different from the Canadian one is useful in predicting the effects of the relatively limited types of health services reform which constitute the set of realistic short-term options. For many issues cross-country evidence of the type that we will be discussing here may not be a good substitute for research on Canadian data, experimental or non-experimental. On the other hand, with a somewhat longer-term perspective, institutional arrangements need not be regarded as fixed, and if the purpose is to predict the effect of as yet untried forms of institutional change, there is no choice but to draw one's evidence from elsewhere. Hence, for considering the broader philosophical issue that we are concerned with here, namely whether in the long run, Canada's health care system would be better served by making more, or less, use of the market mechanism, evidence from countries otherwise similar to Canada but with different health care institutions, provides a good, if not the only, starting point.

A market case—the United States

As usual, the kinds of data one wants is one thing; what is available is another. On the "market side", the U.S. is the obvious choice: it is about the only country in the world with a per capita income comparable to Canada's *and* with a substantially market-oriented health care system. Even so, one may raise questions about the relevance of the U.S. experience. For example, is the apparent degree of inequality in the U.S. health services consumption an inherent characteristic of a market-oriented system, or does it simply reflect a lesser concern for equality in general in the U.S.? We will return to this question below.

A non-market case—the United Kingdom

On the non-market side, the choice is less obvious. The U.K. and Sweden are both examples of industrialized countries with health services systems that are less market-oriented than the Canadian one. A casual impression from the data indicates that the Swedish system is successful in delivering high-quality care, but it is quite costly. An equally casual impression from the U.K. gives a mixed picture with respect to effectiveness, but the cost of the health services system has been kept at a very low level relative to that of the U.S. or Canada. At the same time, one must bear in mind that the U.K. has a considerably lower per capita income than either Sweden or Canada, and I will return below to the question of the effect this might have on the comparisons. In the end, I chose the U.K. as the principal standard of comparison for data reasons: while data are scarce in either case, there is relatively speaking more easily available information on the U.K. The Swedish case is interesting as an example of a centralized system that is considerably more costly than the U.K. one, however, and I will comment in an Appendix on the difference it would have made if Sweden had been chosen rather than the U.K.

The chapter is organized as follows. I begin by giving a comparative description of the institutional organization of the health care system in the U.K., U.S., and Canada. I then go on to the information about differences in the resources used in health care production in the three countries, and compare the total cost of the systems. While information on the output, i.e., the "health" of the population, is notoriously hard to come by, I will discuss the partial indices and casual information that *is* available. Finally, I consider the question of current trends in health care policy in the U.S. and the U.K., and draw some conclusions in relation to the current Canadian debate.

II. HEALTH INSURANCE IN THE UNITED KINGDOM

A. BASIC ELEMENTS
OF THE U.K. HEALTH SYSTEM

'Free' medical care since 1948

I start with the simplest case, namely that of the National Health Service (NHS) in the U.K. This organization was started in 1948 to replace a mixed system in which part of the population was covered by National Health Insurance, but other parts either had voluntary private coverage or no coverage at all.[1] The basic principle of the NHS is a simple one: with certain minor exceptions, everybody in Britain is entitled to any kind of required medical treatment for any condition, free of charge. All costs of treatment are paid by the NHS which receives the bulk of its revenue directly from the government: at the present time, about 85 per cent comes directly out of general revenue, 10 per cent from compulsory social insurance payments collected by the government, and only 5 per cent from patients, representing the cost of certain drugs and services not covered by the NHS. Hence, even though the NHS is equivalent to universal, comprehensive, compulsory health insurance, there is no explicit premium system, and there can be no "opting out". Those who purchase private health insurance in effect pay twice—first for their private coverage and second, through taxes and social security payments, for their NHS coverage; even so, a surprisingly large number of people continue to buy private insurance, and I will come back to the reasons for this later on.

Hospitals nationalized

The second set of important changes of the system in 1948 (i.e., apart from making coverage universal) was on the supply side of health services. All hospitals were nationalized. Up until 1948, public health insurance did not cover in-patient hospital care. As a consequence, British hospitals (owned primarily by voluntary associations or local governments) were in financial trouble and for that reason little or no expansion of hospital capacity, or modernization of existing facilities, was taking place. The British Ministry of Health took full responsibility for operating and capital costs of hospitals as of 1948.

Doctors' incomes controlled

Extensive negotiations took place between the government and the British Medical Association regarding the method of paying physicians. Under the earlier National Health Insurance scheme, those covered under it had their G.P. services paid for by capitation, i.e., the doctor was under contract to provide all necessary services in return for a fixed annual or monthly fee per patient on his list; this in turn was a continuation of similar arrangements that had existed between G.P.s and some voluntary associations even before National Health Insurance was enacted in 1911. Most doctors in 1948 were still deriving part of their income on a fee-for-service basis, however, from people not covered by National Health Insurance. The method actually chosen in the National Health Service reform was to continue the capitation principle: the BMA favoured it as an alternative to straight salary (i.e., with the G.P.s employed by the NHS) which, it appeared, was what the government had in mind. The government, on the other hand, was not prepared to pay the G.P.s on a fee-for-service basis, which otherwise would have been the method favoured by the doctors.[2] In contrast to general practitioners, specialist doctors working in the hospitals were to be paid on a salary basis. Under the current system, many of the specialists work only part-time as salaried hospital doctors and supplement their income by part-time private practice on a fee-for-service basis.

At the present time, virtually the entire U.K. population uses the NHS and is registered with a G.P. under it. The method of paying the G.P. basically remains that of a capitation fee paid by the NHS, though it has been modified somewhat to bring it closer to a salary system: in addition to the capitation fee, the doctors are paid a "basic practice allowance" (i.e., a salary); they are further paid an additional amount if they practice in an underserviced area, if they are part of a group practice, for seniority, etc. As a consequence of these modifications, the average G.P. derives a substantial proportion (perhaps as much as 50 per cent) of his income from sources other than capitation. Part of the reason for changing the system in the direction of less reliance on the capitation component appears to have been to avoid compromising the quality of care which might suffer if some doctors are induced to take responsibility for too many patients. The capitation payments are intended to cover only the doctors' services: doctors are directly reimbursed for rent and rates of practice premises, and for expenditure on ancillary staff, but expenses for diagnostic hospital tests, hospitalization, and specialist treatment recommended by the G.P. are borne entirely by the NHS and involves no cost to either the doctor or the patient. It is interesting to note that the G.P. (rather than the patient) has the major responsibility for the decision to seek treatment in a hospital or by a specialist: "patients are not usually accepted by hospitals without a family doctor's recommendation." [3]

Public health standards lower?

In addition to health services provided free of charge by the NHS, a not inconsiderable amount is also provided on a fee-paying basis outside of the NHS. One source gives total in-patient accommodation for "private" patients as 7 per cent of that for NHS patients, and total national expenditure on private health care was roughly estimated in 1973 to about 2 per cent of total NHS expenditure. [4] Another estimate states that about 4 per cent of the population continue to use privately produced medical care as their "normal" practice.[5] In addition, there is a substantial amount of health services provided for a fee to people from overseas (casual evidence indicates that Britain exports a good deal of medical services to high-income people from low-income countries).

According to a British Government pamphlet, the main motives of U.K. residents who prefer private treatment "appear to be the wish for greater freedom in arranging consultations and hospital admissions at times convenient to themselves, the desire for privacy, and the wish to be treated by a consultant of their choice". In a masterpiece of diplomatic phrasing, the pamphlet then adds a comment on a sensitive subject: "There is *no* evidence that private treatment is *often* sought in the belief that the standard of medical care will be higher than that under the NHS".[6] (Italics added.) Whether or not this statement makes sense would seem to depend on one's definition of the "standard of medical care". Privacy, freedom of choice with respect to which doctor to go to, and shorter waiting times for hospital admission may not be irrelevant for the public's judgement of "standards". In any event, the end result is that a small, high-income minority have elected to arrange their own medical care because they are willing to pay for the convenience of dealing with independent providers. For the vast majority of the population, however, the price is too high, and most people thus rely on the NHS even though it may not offer this convenience. Some observers have described this system as one of "dual standards of medical care", and the extent to which the existence of private medicine conflicts with an egalitarian ideology has been vigorously debated from time to time.

The main features summarized

Disregarding the private health services sector which after all is quite small, one may now summarize the main features of the present British health services system. *First,* it has compulsory, universal and comprehensive public-sector health insurance financed essentially out of general tax revenue. *Second,* health services are provided directly by a single public sector organization which owns the hospitals and pays the doctors on a mixed salary and capitation basis.

B. HOW RESOURCES ARE ALLOCATED
   IN THE U.K. SYSTEM

Consider now the question how resources are allocated in this system. With respect to the overall amount of resources spent on health services, the decision is ultimately a political one, with the Government and Parliament annually debating the NHS budget. As I will discuss later, even though total costs have grown rapidly in Britain as elsewhere, they still appear quite low relative to the U.S. and Canada. I will also return to the question whether the relatively low spending faithfully represents the citizens' willingness to pay for health services, or whether they would have been willing to pay for more health services if they could have had them.

Bureaucratic decisions, political guidelines and budget constraints

Given the overall budget, and presumably subject to politically determined guidelines, the allocation to specific services and their geographical distribution is essentially determined by the NHS administration. It was originally subdivided into three main administrative units along functional lines, responsible for hospital services, primary care (i.e., payment of G.P.s), and community health and normal social services.[7] There was a further decentralization to regional and local levels, but the functional division persisted at these levels as well. As might be expected, this administrative arrangement led to frictions and bureaucratic problems. G.P.s had little influence as to which diagnostic, hospital, and specialist services would be available in their area, so that there arose shortages for certain facilities with resulting problems of queuing and waiting lists, with other facilities being under-utilized. Conversely, the hospital administration had no way of influencing the allocation of G.P.s or to influence G.P. decisions with respect to utilization of various services, for example, to impress upon them the desirability of avoiding costly diagnostic procedures.

The attempt to decentralize

As a consequence of these problems, a major reorganization of the decision-making structure was undertaken in 1974. The objective was to "integrate (the) tripartite structure into a *geographical organization*" with management roles delegated to multi-professional teams which would include hospital administrators, clinicians, Medical Officers of Health, and with input from lay people. A major training program was mounted to prepare clinicians, medical officers, etc., for their new managerial roles. There is not yet a great deal of information available about how well the new system has functioned, but it seems a safe bet to guess that the cost of better decisions (if they are better) by integrated teams, in terms of added training requirements and administrative workload, especially on medical professionals, has been pretty heavy.

A market analogue?

The problem of designing a well-functioning system to administer a giant organization such as the NHS is an intriguing one. Ideally, a decentralized system such as is now being implemented should lead to an allocation of resources at the local level that is efficient and flexible from the viewpoint of responding to health needs of the local population, (as assessed jointly by the members of the health-professional teams), and the central allocation of funds between regions should similarly be systematically determined on the basis of health needs. But there are numerous difficulties in practice. For example, just how are "health needs" to be measured? Will it be possible for the central administration to exercise effective control over cost without interfering with the detailed decisions at the local level, or will the system be a slow and cumbersome one in which each decision has to be considered at several levels? Can one design a system which rewards efficiency and cost cutting at the local level, or will the incentive on each local unit be to always ask for the largest possible budget? Can the system be kept free from political meddling? Will the bureaucracy be flexible enough to select the best personnel at the various levels or will there be problems with incompetent managers and officials holding on to their positions by force of seniority or political influence?

Complete centralization of the health services system along U.K. lines presumably is undertaken to resolve the problem of universal access to the health care system. But it simultaneously raises a whole set of formidable problems of flexibility and efficient decentralized decision-making which may have no good solutions. The market mechanism, on the other hand, provides a more or less ready-made and flexible system to accomplish decentralization. What the U.K. experience indicates in this respect, it seems to me, is that if a solution to the equitability-of-access problem could be found *within* the market framework, the pay-offs in terms of avoided administrative headaches could be very substantial.

III. HEALTH INSURANCE IN THE U.S.

A. BASIC ELEMENTS OF THE U.S. HEALTH INSURANCE SYSTEM

We turn now to the polar case to that of the U.K., the strongly market-oriented health care system in the U.S.

Absence of universal health insurance
From the viewpoint of the individual patient, the most important difference between the systems presumably is the absence of universal health insurance: if you need medical care in the U.S., you either pay directly for the services, or you make arrangements in advance for private insurance coverage (except those qualifying under one of the public plans: see below). From the individual's viewpoint, therefore, the organization and performance of the health insurance industry is of paramount importance.

The U.S. health insurance industry has a great deal of diversity. There are over 1,000 private carriers (mostly life insurance companies) selling health insurance, but there is considerable concentration: around 1970, the top 20 companies accounted for nearly three-quarters of the premium volume of private carriers.[8] Two of the largest plans, Blue Cross and Blue Shield, are not classified as private carriers but are non-profit organizations with tax-exempt status. They are closely affiliated with the hospitals and medical societies, especially Blue Cross which has a substantial proportion of people with health care systems affiliation on its board of directors. It has sometimes been maintained that the Blue plans have been organized more to protect the interests of the providers rather than those of the consumers of health care; we will return to this question below.

Universal government protection for the old, welfare recipients and the "medically indigent"

Since the mid-1960s, the U.S. Federal Government is the third largest participant in the insurance field, through the Medicare plan. The plan has two components; part A which automatically covers all Social Security beneficiaries over age 65 for "extensive hospital expenses", and part B which is voluntary and, in return for a fixed premium, covers part A beneficiaries for most medical services provided by physicans and others. The vast majority of those entitled to Medicare have chosen to enroll in the voluntary part of the plan. While the U.S. government is financially responsible for Medicare, it is administered (i.e., premiums are collected and benefits paid) by the Blue Plans and some private carriers. In addition, the Federal government, together with the State governments, through Medicaid, pays for the health services consumption of welfare recipients and other "medically indigent".

Prepaid group insurance plans

Some individuals, finally, are protected by a variety of "independent" plans, including the prepaid group plans, union group plans, individual practice plans, etc. Prepaid group plans are the largest in this category, comprising about 1.5 to 2 per cent of all insured in 1970. They provide a wide range of health services free of charge in return for a fixed periodical subscription. Individual practice plans (covering about 1 per cent of all insured) are similar to the Blue Shield plans (which primarily cover physician services, not hospital services), but are organized by groups of physicians who in effect act as insurers: they provide services free of charge to the patient, through their individual practices, in return for a fixed subscription to the plan. The physician then collects his fee from the plan.

95 per cent of Americans have some insurance coverage

Accurate and recent statistics on health insurance enrollment are hard to obtain, and in any event are difficult to interpret because of wide variations in coverage depending on the type of plan, etc.

The broad picture, however, is clear. In 1950, less than half the U.S. population was covered by any form of hospital or medical insurance. By 1970, the proportion of those having no coverage at all, either from private or public plans, had fallen to around 10 to 15 per cent; if those who are eligible for protection by institutional plans (such as Medicaid) are excluded, the proportion who are not covered falls further to around 5 per cent. Between 85 to 90 per cent of the population had coverage against hospitalization; this figure included only about 10 per cent insured under Medicare, so that by far the largest factor in explaining the increase from 1950 was the growth in voluntary private coverage. In 1950, the number protected by "comprehensive health insurance", which includes hospitalization, surgery, and treatment by physicians, was negligible; in 1970, about 55 per cent of the population was so covered. The growth of the health insurance industry has been truly remarkable, and one can safely assume that it has continued during the 1970s, even though the rate of growth is bound to slow down as more and more people already have comprehensive coverage.[9]

Type of insurance in force varies widely
An evaluation of a private health insurance system, however, cannot be based on aggregative statistics on numbers of people covered only. In contrast to compulsory public insurance which tends to be almost completely comprehensive (in the sense of covering any amount of expenditures for almost any type of health services) at a uniform cost to the individual, the health insurance provided by the private sector in the U.S. varies widely in terms of various kinds of coverage which are excluded, maximum liability limits, deductibles and, above all, in the cost to the patient.

B. INSURANCE COVERAGE AND CONSUMER CHOICE

In Chapter One I argued that when given the choice, many individuals in a market system might find it to their advantage to undertake some degree of self-insurance by covering themselves only against serious illness requiring costly treatment. There are several ways in which partial self-insurance may be accomplished. *First,* comprehensive policies can be written with deductibles and co-insurance provisions. Most private policies in the U.S. do indeed have such features: 80-20 co-insurance provisions (i.e., with the insured paying 20 per cent of covered expenses) are common, and there are a variety of deductible provisions with the patient being responsible for a specified maximum amount of expenditure per year or quarter, or per illness episode; sometimes the deductible refers only to non-hospital expenditure, and so on. *Second,* the patient may carry part of the risk by insuring himself only against the cost of certain *types* of services. Health insurance in the U.S. has traditionally been subdivided into three main categories: hospitalization insurance, typically covering "room and board charges" and a limited range of ancillary services; hospital plus surgical insurance, which includes specified surgical procedures, principally those provided on an inpatient basis; and major medical, which covers "most of the rest", including visits to a physician's office, etc. As noted above, while about 90 per cent of the U.S. population has at least one of the above types of coverage, only about 55 per cent has all three.

The cost of savings from deductibles

Deductible provisions and exclusion of certain services generally have quite a dramatic effect on the premium cost to the consumer. One estimate by a major insurance company in 1971 indicated that the premium for a $600 group policy with a $100/person deductible would be reduced to less than $300 if the deductible were increased to $500/person. In another example an instance is cited where the elimination of a $400 deductible would increase the premium of a group policy by $350.[9A] Part of the reason for the high cost of low deductibles, of course, is that the expected value of claims for, say, the first $500 worth of coverage is much higher than the second $500, and so on. In 1969, a group of health insurance companies reported that 40 to 60 per cent of the number of claims they handled were less than $100; on the other hand, it was estimated that only about 7 per cent of the insured public filed claims in excess of $500. But another major contributing factor is the very high administration cost for small claims, which may amount to as much as 20 per cent of that part of the premium corresponding to the first $500 worth of coverage. Thus, from the insured person's point of view a certain amount of self-insurance in the form of a sizable deductible may well pay off because so much of the premium reduction reflects savings in administration costs. Similar comments apply to the exclusion of ''minor'' services, such as office visits to a family doctor, say.

Does insurance protect the consumer or the health services provider?

The existence of co-insurance and deductibles is pretty much in agreement with what one would expect in the light of the discussion in Chapter One: they give the consumer an opportunity to save money by taking more responsibility on himself for his consumption decisions when the situation is not totally critical and he has some real choice. But it should also be recognized that there are many common features in U.S. health insurance contracts that are difficult to explain in terms of what the patient wants, and which rather seem to represent the interest of the providers, or of the insurance companies. The co-insurance provisions in many plans apply only for payments *above* certain limits, i.e., if you have coverage for a specified procedure or illness, the plan may cover 100 per cent of a stated basic amount but only 80 per cent of what you have to pay in excess of that amount if for some reason the cost in your particular case is higher. Given that the general objective of insurance is to protect the individual against hardship if he is unusually unlucky (i.e., in this case if the cost is substantially higher than the basic amount), it is unusual to find co-insurance provisions that provide full protection if a person is lucky but otherwise only partial protection. To some extent, this feature may be explained by the influence of the Blue-Cross/Blue Shield plans which in the past provided ''first-dollar'' coverage, i.e., had a zero deductible. As was noted above, the interests of the medical and hospital associations have been well represented in formulating the terms of these plans, and the co-insurance provisions just noted make more sense when seen in this light: they protect not the unlucky patient but the unlucky doctor or hospital, as it were.

Even though most health insurance policies have deductibles, they are generally quite small (say, the first 100 dollars only are excluded). Again, one may speculate that this may be due partly to the early influence of Blue Shield/Blue Cross: from the point of view of the health services provider, a low or zero deductible is an advantage, because it saves him the trouble of individually billing and collecting from the large number of patients who would not exceed the deductible if it were more substantial.

Provisions for long-term illness

Most health insurance policies also contain a variety of exclusions for illnesses that require long-term treatment at high cost. Thus Krizay and Wilson, in their study of U.S. health insurance, list psychiatric care, renal dialysis, treatment for drug addiction and alcoholism, and treatment which is covered, even if only in part, by Workmen's Compensation among the common ones in private policies. Various policies contain limitations on the daily amount of hospital charges reimbursed, maximum number of treatments for a given condition, and maximum number of days in hospital per illness, etc. In addition, and perhaps most seriously, many private policies contain some limitation on the maximum dollar liability of the company; these are sometimes stated as an annual maximum, sometimes as a life-time maximum, and sometimes both. With the increasing use of highly sophisticated but also very expensive methods of treatment for various types of disease or injury, there are now many instances where a person may reach the limit of his coverage in a single serious illness episode or accident. In recent years, some companies have abandoned maximum liability specifications of this kind (they formerly were contained in most private policies), presumably in recognition of this problem and perhaps also in response to the call for a U.S. national health insurance scheme with no such limitations. But many policies with relatively low upper limits are still marketed, so that even persons with comprehensive coverage may not be protected against financial disaster in a really serious situation.

Lower limits and more numerous exclusions presumably reduce the expected cost to the insurance company and hence the insurance can be sold at lower premium levels: you get what you pay for, the companies would say. At the same time, however, it is not easy for the average consumer to evaluate what he is in fact getting. The list of exclusions under a policy is often couched in terms of technical language and the consumer probably does not have very good information about either the incidence probability or the cost of the kinds of serious illness to which the upper limits might become applicable. A strict libertarian would say that individuals who wish to leave themselves unprotected by insurance against real disasters, should be free to do so. In my personal judgment, this is one of the instances where one should question this principle, because of the consumer's imperfect information, and also because uninsured individuals with really serious conditions are likely to get treatment at public expense in any event; I will return to this issue in Chapter Three.

The cost of insurance

On the question of the cost to the consumer of health insurance in the U.S., generalization is difficult because of the wide variety of policies in existence. It appears to be true, however, that premium levels have been rising rapidly in recent years. A problem which is attracting increasing attention is the very high cost of individual coverage in comparison with similar coverage through group plans. Krizay and Wilson give an estimate where the premium cost of individual coverage through a comprehensive package for a family of four is more than twice as high as the same coverage through a group plan. Again, one may speculate that this differential is due to the higher administration costs of individual policies, but it may also reflect differential selling costs, as well as different bargaining power between buyers of group plans (unions, large employers) and individuals. If competition between insurance companies is sufficiently intense the latter factor shouldn't matter, but it is uncertain how intense it is, in fact, in the market for individual policies. The large companies appear to concentrate primarily on group policies, whereas the small companies are more important in the market for individual policies; a possible explanation for the high cost of the latter may be higher profits or, more likely, higher costs in the small companies.

Profits in health insurance

Critics of the present institutional form of the U.S. health insurance system have occasionally claimed that the rising premium costs are to be explained by the high and rising profits of health insurance companies. Available data on profits in the industry as a whole make it difficult to substantiate this claim. Estimates from the late 1960s indicate that, most of the time, the sum of claims and operating costs were higher than accrued premium incomes. While this figure must be corrected for investment earnings on reserves (premiums are prepaid) and the time lag between time of illness and payment of the claim, the estimates of reserves in relation to premiums make it clear that this correction would not alter the major conclusion that profits of insurance companies reflect at best a very minor part of the premium cost to the consumer.

Thus, competition appears to have been at least sufficiently effective to preclude "excess profits" to any major extent. The existence of the Blue plans has probably contributed to this in several ways. First, since they are non-profit institutions wholly engaged in health insurance, any (tax-exempt) profits which they make on their operations are passed on to the insured in the form of lower rates. Secondly, since they deal directly with the providers (i.e., hospitals and doctors), they have on occasion been able to exert pressure on them to accept fees negotiated in advance between the plan and the provider as payment in full for the services, which also has tended to indirectly lower the premium rates. The private companies have had to operate efficiently in order to be competitive with rates set in this way.

On the other hand, competition from conventional insurance companies has ultimately forced the Blue plans to abandon the principle of setting rates according to "community ratings". This principle meant that premiums for a given coverage were uniform across individuals but variable across communities, since they were set according to the expected health services consumption in the community as a whole. The private insurance companies, operating on a national basis, instead used "experience ratings" which varied across individuals but were the same across communities. This principle would tend to produce lower rates for low-risk individuals (for example, younger people with little previous illness) but higher rates for high-risk persons (principally the aged). The Blue plans thus faced the prospect of becoming the residual insurer for high-risk individuals, and in the end had to abandon the community rating principle. The introduction of Medicare and Medicaid can be seen in part as a response to this development: under the experience rating system, health insurance for the aged and those with a history of illness had become prohibitively high, given their often very limited income.

Health Maintenance Organizations

Finally, as was noted above, a small percentage (less than 3 per cent) of the population covered by voluntary insurance in the U.S. have coverage through some form of Health Maintenance Organization or prepaid group practice plan. The general principle behind those plans was discussed in the previous chapter: they are arrangements under which the insurance function and the provision of health services are combined, so that a fixed periodic subscription to the prepaid plan takes the place of the insurance premium that the consumer (or, more frequently, his employer) would have paid for conventional insurance; the health services covered under the plan are then provided to the consumer free of charge.

How do prepaid plans compare with other forms of coverage in terms of cost? The evidence is scanty, but whatever is available seems to indicate that they compare quite favourably. A study in California in the mid-sixties, (in which an allowance was made for differences in coverage by including estimated consumer expenditure outside the plans), indicated that, on the average, the premium cost plus out-of-pocket expenditure by consumers covered by the Kaiser—Permanente group practice plan were between 75 and 90 per cent of those covered by conventional plans. While the non-uniformity of coverage means that the group practice plans will not necessarily be the most favourable to consumers in all cases, Krizay and Wilson nevertheless showed that for a variety of hypothetical utilization patterns, the group practice plans were less costly to the patient than conventional insurance. As we will discuss later on, the main reason for the apparent advantage of these plans seems to be the fact that doctors in group plans have tended to hospitalize their patients at a significantly lower rate than independent doctors.[10] Somewhat similar results have been found for the case of the "individual practice plans" referred to above. An additional source of possible savings from group plans is the lower administration cost: the cost of handling individual claims represents the major component of the administration cost of private insurance carriers, and tends to be around 10 per cent of the cost of insurance. Claims handling is essentially eliminated under group practice plans, and, as an example, the administration cost of the Kaiser—Permanente plan in 1969 represented just over 3 per cent of total costs.

Given this apparent cost advantage of prepayment plans and the rapid increase in the price of conventional insurance, one may ask why the growth of such plans has not been faster than in fact it has been: after all, 3 per cent of the population still represents a fairly small minority. In part, the answer may simply be that consumers are willing to pay a bit more for conventional insurance. In prepayment plans, coverage is typically limited to the cost of the services provided by the doctors employed by the plan, so that the patients' choice of physician (and also of hospital) is restricted. While group practice may offer a certain amount of added convenience when they have GPs and specialists located in the same place, often in a clinic or a hospital where diagnostic tests, etc., can be carried out, some people who have used them have complained about a lack of the kind of individual attention to patients that an independent family doctor would give. A more important explanation, however, is probably the resistance of organized medicine, to which I referred in Chapter One, against the prepayment plans. This resistance has probably prevented more plans from being started, and perhaps led to some reluctance on the part of good doctors to accept employment with the existing plans.

C. HOW WELL DOES PRIVATE INSURANCE WORK?

In the light of the foregoing description, what can be said in general about the efficiency with which the market-oriented health insurance system in the U.S. solves the problem of making medical care accessible to the population and providing protection against the economic consequences of ill health? On the plus side, the enormous growth in voluntary insurance since World War II is an indication that the increasingly costly treatment methods developed by medical technology have by and large become available to the majority of the population through insurance, rather than having been restricted to "the rich". Furthermore, the intensity of competition between insurance providers has been strong enough to keep premiums in line with the actual cost of health services: the rapidly rising premium levels have been due to rising costs of claims and administration, not to rising profits of insurance companies. The consumer has had a wide range of choice between different degrees of coverage. As I argued in Chapter One, freedom for the consumer to choose the extent and form of his insurance protection may be an essential pre-condition for the supply-demand mechanism to work effectively in the health services sector.

On the other hand, for many people, their financial means at the time of illness may importantly influence the kind of care they will get. Some only have protection against specific types of treatment, such as hospitalization, or no coverage at all. Limits and exclusions of various kinds may mean heavy direct expenditures on health care consumption even for individuals who do have insurance. The large variety of insurance contract types may not entirely represent an advantage: it may also represent wasteful competition through product differentiation in preference to the more intense price competition which would result with a more standardized commodity, especially with respect to exclusions and upper limits. For people in high-risk categories, such as the aged or those with a previous history of illness, competition between private insurance providers made the situation worse, not better: to compete for the low-risk market, they had to lower premiums in low-risk categories and raise them (or simply deny insurance) to high-risk individuals. In fact, of course, the problem of health insurance for the aged finally was considered severe enough so that for this patient category, the market system was supplanted by Medicare, and similarly, concern about access to care by low-income welfare recipients led to Medicaid. Further, the market system has favoured those enrolled in group plans: the high cost for those who cannot get group protection is probably an important explanation why a not insignificant minority of the U.S. population still is not covered by any kind of insurance, or only covered to a very limited extent.

Thus, the overall judgment on the present system must be mixed, and in spite of its dramatic improvement, the degree to which the population is protected still cannot be compared to that in systems with universal public insurance. Not surprisingly, the question of some form of National Health Insurance has been high on the political agenda in the U.S. for a long time, and given the pronouncements of the Carter Administration to this effect, it is probably safe to predict that legislation proposing some form of universal coverage will be introduced in the reasonably near future.

D. THE SUPPLY OF HEALTH SERVICES IN THE U.S.

With the exception of the relatively small number of doctors who are employed by hospitals in the private or public sector, or who provide their services within the framework of some form of prepayment plan, physicians in the U.S. are paid under the fee-for-service system either by billing their patients or, in some cases, their patients' insurance companies directly. Similarly, with the exception of a limited number of hospitals operated by the government and providing care to special groups (such as members of the armed forces) or those operated by Health Maintenance Organizations, hospitals in the U.S. are financially independent institutions which derive their entire revenue from fees charged for services performed.

i. The market for doctors' services

Considering first the market for physician services, it was argued in Chapter One that the degree of competitiveness in this market would depend to a large extent on the prevailing type of health insurance coverage among the doctors' patients. As just indicated, since the 1950s there has been a very rapid expansion in the proportion of the U.S. population which is covered against the cost of physician services, both through private plans and through public plans such as Medicare and Medicaid. Most of this growth has been through conventional insurance which puts no restriction on the patient's choice of physician, so that for an individual with full insurance coverage, the fee charged by the doctor is of no relevance at all to his choice of doctor. The only remaining motivation to engage in price competition arises from insurance provisions such as limits on the fee covered for a given service, co-insurance, or patients with deductibles, or from the desire to attract the diminishing group of patients without insurance coverage. These factors have not been strong enough to prevent a spectacular increase in physician incomes in the U.S. to parallel the rapid growth in health insurance coverage.

The impact of insurance companies on competitiveness

Apart from specifying co-insurance, deductibles, and limits of coverage, conventional health insurance carriers have not been making major efforts to influence physician fees. The Blue Shield organization and Medicare have tried to some extent: the Blue Shield plans at one time employed a system of fee schedules according to which participating physicians were reimbursed. However, the physician was not compelled to accept this fee as payment in full, but was free to bill the patient directly for additional amounts. Under the current Blue Shield plans, participating physicians, i.e., those who are paid directly by the plan without billing the patient, are compelled to accept the Blue Shield reimbursement as payment in full, and the plan will only agree to pay a "usual, customary and reasonable" fee which is determined with reference to the prevailing fee distribution among participating physicians in the region. Doctors who wish to be paid directly by Medicare have to accept a similar arrangement.

These provisions may have put some damper on the tendency for fee increases. There is, however, also some evidence that they have led to various manipulations by physicians in determining the charge, by varying the description of the service or in some cases even by letting the choice of procedure to be performed be influenced by the fee structure. The general impression one gets from the literature is that insurance agencies generally have not been very successful at policing of fees in order to hold costs down. Nor, one suspects, have they been particularly successful in ensuring that only "medically necessary" procedures have been undertaken, and there is some evidence that the "demand creation" for physician services, to which I referred in Chapter One, has been present in the U.S., particularly for surgery.

The creation of demand for health services

A study by C. Lewis, published in 1969,[11] found large regional variations in the rates of six common surgical procedures (tonsillectomy with adenoidectomy, appendectomy, hernia repair, hemorrhoidectomy, cholecystectomy, varicose veins). In attempting to explain these differentials, he found statistically significant positive correlations between the surgery rates and either the number of certified surgeons or the number of surgeons and GPs taken together, or both, in four out of the six cases. While this may mean that there were many people in the low-rate regions who ''needed'' operations but did not get them because there weren't enough doctors, it is equally plausible to argue that many of the operations in the high-rate regions were not urgently needed but simply reflected the ready availability of surgeons. Other studies from the 1960s and early 1970s support these arguments. Some physicians estimate that 75 per cent of tonsillectomies are unnecessary; a medical audit in California found that the number of hysterectomies performed by a group of doctors increased five-fold when they were switched from salary to fee-for-service reimbursement.[11A] While these studies are somewhat dated, it is unlikely that the situation has changed much since the early 1970s. The incentives to perform more surgery may in fact have been somewhat strengthened through the introduction of Medicare and Medicaid under which reimbursement for operations on low-income people is now ensured.

Organized medicine and competition

As I discussed in Chapter One, the actions of organized medicine may also be important in influencing the degree of competition in the market for physician services. In the U.S., the American Medical Association has generally been considered as a highly influential and politically active organization. A study from the mid-sixties reports that it was then maintaining a staff of twenty-three lobbyists in Washington and some seventy publicists in its headquarters, and a *New York Times* report referring to 1974 stated that the A.M.A. spent more to finance political candidates than any group except the A.F.L.-C.I.O.[11B] Partly as a result of this political activity, there has been little public questioning of the A.M.A.'s methods of regulating the practice of medicine, and some of the policies it has followed have clearly had the effect of reducing competition among physicians. I referred in Chapter One to its success in enforcing a ban on the publication by doctors of any kind of fee information, or more generally, on any kind of advertising by doctors on the grounds that it is "unethical". I also discussed the very forceful resistance that it has mounted against widespread use of other methods of paying the doctor than fee-for-service. Finally, as will be discussed below, there is little evidence that the supply of doctors has expanded at a significantly higher rate in response to rising doctors' incomes.

Strict rules on the accreditation of medical schools have been maintained by the A.M.A. and as a consequence, the capacity of the system to train additional physicians has expanded only slowly. Hence, even though average physician incomes in the U.S. have risen dramatically over the past fifteen years, the supply of physicians has not risen very fast, at least not in comparison with Canada,[12] and there has been a chronic excess demand for admission to medical schools. While it may be true that this relatively slow increase has been necessary in order to prevent a deterioration in quality, it is at least as plausible to conclude that it simply represents a successful attempt by an interest group to restrict the supply of its services in order to maintain a high average income level.

ii. The market for hospital services

From the point of view of total cost, the market for hospital services is of even greater importance than that for doctors. The U.S. system of hospital services is based primarily on independently operated hospitals, some organized to make profits for their owners, but the large majority being non-profit institutions. While some of their operating revenue and capital funds for expansion are derived from direct cash grants from various levels of government, by far the largest proportion of their income comes from charges to patients or their insurers for services performed, and the proportion coming from this source has been increasing in the 1960s and 1970s, especially after the introduction of Medicare and Medicaid.

Competition and insurance plans

The question of the form of competition between independent hospitals in a fee-for-service system and the influence of health insurance was discussed at some length in Chapter One. As was observed there, since hospitals do not compete directly for patients but rather for doctors who send their patients to hospitals, it is not clear how effective it would be for them to compete via maintaining low charges. With the extension of hospital insurance to the vast majority of the population (Medicare being particularly important in this respect), the motive to do so has now largely disappeared, and doctors can now make this decision as if the cost to the patient were zero. The burden of coping with hospital charges thus has fallen to an increasing extent on the insurers who have had to raise their premiums when the charges rise.

The conventional carriers have not been involved in this issue, since they deal only with the insured patients, not with the hospitals. The Blue Cross and Medicare plans, however, have tried to negotiate with the hospitals regarding fee policies and measures to counteract rising costs. Unlike physicians, hospitals participating in these plans typically do accept insurance reimbursements as payment in full and do not bill patients for additional amounts, so that the plans have some potential leverage over charges, and state government insurance regulations have sometimes been used to induce Blue Cross plans to put pressure on hospitals to reduce charges by denying approval for Blue Cross rate increases.[13] The effectiveness of this approach is limited by the fact that Blue Cross cannot force the hospitals to participate in their plans and if a hospital elects not to participate, they are no longer obliged to accept the Blue Cross rates as payment in full. Hence, while Blue Cross may have been effective in preventing individual participating hospitals from getting out of line, by basing their reimbursement rates on prevailing or average charges for hospitals in the plan region, it has probably not had a major impact on the increases in the average level of charges of hospitals in general.

The potential influence of the Medicare plan is greater, because of the convenience to the hospitals of being reimbursed directly for services to the elderly who on the average have higher hospital charges and lower incomes than the rest of the population. Medicare has also been somewhat successful in making the hospitals agree to reductions in reimbursement rates under the plan, by being somewhat restrictive in the definition of the actual cost of the services performed.

How do U.S. hospitals compete?

If hospitals do not compete for business by maintaining low fees, how do they compete? As was discussed in Chapter One, one way in which they can do it is by continually upgrading the range and quality of the services they provide, not only with respect to basic "hotel services", but also, and more importantly, ancillary services of various kinds such as advanced radiology equipment, intensive care units, etc. From the administrator's point of view, this kind of strategy is appealing in many ways: in addition to being more efficient in attracting patients than a low-charge policy, it makes it easier for him to attract high-quality medical staff. The fact that most hospitals in the U.S. are operated on a non-profit basis may also have contributed to this process. Other things equal, hospital managers are likely to prefer being in charge of an institution possessing the most advanced technology; with no stockholders breathing down their necks about the rate of return on their investment, they have more freedom to spend money acquiring advanced equipment even if it is not "economically viable". The U.S. literature contains frequent references to tendencies for costly duplication of expensive equipment in the hospital system, and the data on rapidly rising costs per bed-day provide convincing evidence that these factors have had a good deal of influence during the 1960s and 1970s.[14]

iii. A summary of the main features

We may now turn to a brief summary of the main characteristics of the institutional organization of the supply side of the U.S. health services industry. By far the largest proportion of all services is still supplied by independent doctors and hospitals operating on a fee-for-service basis. As would be expected, for the reasons discussed in Chapter One, the rapid growth of voluntary health insurance and perhaps more significantly, the introduction of subsidized insurance via Medicare and Medicaid, have led to a weakening of price competition and to rapidly rising costs.

Organized medicine in the U.S. is politically powerful, and it appears fairly clear that its activities have further weakened the effectiveness of competition in the market for health services. In an earlier era, most of its efforts were directed at controlling the degree of fee competition between individual physicians, and at controlling the expansion in the supply of the number of physicians. With the growth of health insurance, its interests have increasingly become focussed on preserving the fee-for-service system as the predominant method of paying the doctor, and resisting alternative methods such as prepayment or salary systems; as I argued above, permitting these alternative systems to exist and expand may be a precondition for the competitive process to work effectively in the market for health services.

Finally, it is interesting to observe that organized medicine in the U.S. (and also in Canada, before the advent of public health insurance) has generally been opposed to government-financed universal, comprehensive health insurance. Since I have argued above that a system where everybody has comprehensive insurance is likely to be one in which the incomes of uncontrolled fee-for-service physicians is high, one may wonder why organized medicine has, by and large, opposed it. The answer may well be that the A.M.A. recognizes that an uncontrolled fee-for-service system cannot be maintained under universal public insurance. Sooner or later, it will lead to fee controls (as it has in Canada), or elimination of the fee-for-service system in favour of capitation payments or salary, as it did in the U.K. and as it apparently threatens to do in at least some Canadian provinces. Thus, doctors may well recognize that universal public insurance is not in their interest in the long run.

IV. THE CANADIAN SYSTEM

A. INTRODUCTION

Writing in the *Financial Post* in May 1977, James E. Bennett and Jacques Krasny made the following comment: "By international standards, the Canadian health care system provides excellent quality and abundance of care. Yet, our health resources...are widely misused. The main reason is because resource distribution has been determined largely by market forces, and in the health field, the market seldom, if ever, aligns money and manpower with the real need for care."[15] While they recognize that, especially since the 1960s, the provincial and federal governments have had increasing opportunities to control the health services sector, they appear to imply that little use has been made of these opportunities, and that the health services system we see around us is similar to what it would be under an essentially market-oriented system.

Market failure or market elimination?
I find it very difficult to share that view. To my mind, the present Canadian system rather represents the outcome of a series of government decisions to intervene in the market: by now, it seems more correct to say that the influence of market forces has been virtually eliminated, and (with the partial exception of the services of individual physicians) the process of allocating resources to various parts of the system is essentially a political one. I will try to substantiate this opinion in the following sections.

B. HEALTH INSURANCE IN CANADA

As I will argue below, the present system of public health insurance in Canada, though somewhat different in form, comes pretty close to providing the same degree of universality and comprehensive coverage as does the U.K. National Health Service. The history leading up to this state of affairs is interesting in a number of ways. Constitutionally, public responsibility for the health services sector has been interpreted as falling under provincial jurisdiction, so that direct federal action in this area (with a number of minor exceptions, such as the enforcement of quarantine regulations, provision of health services in the Northwest Territories for the native peoples, and for members of the armed forces) has not been possible. Instead, the federal government has used the method of offering provinces "a deal they couldn't refuse."

Historical roots

Major federal support to general health services dates back to 1948 (the year of the introduction of the U.K. National Health Service), when a program of National Health Grants was initiated.[16] The main activity under that program involved hospital construction, but it also included support for health surveys, professional training, public health research, and tuberculosis control. The intention behind the program was clear: its provisions were seen as being "fundamental prerequisites of a nationwide system of health insurance."[17] As part of the grants' program, a standard accounting and reporting system for Canadian hospitals was established which would later facilitate the introduction of universal public hospital insurance.

It is clear that the Health Grants program had a major impact on the future health services facilities in Canada. When the Hospital Construction Grant program was ended in 1970, it had contributed to the construction of 130,000 beds (out of an estimated total of around 150,000 in the mid-1970s).[18] Its motivation was similar to that which had led to hospital nationalization in the U.K.: with limited health insurance coverage in the population, and hospitals in financial difficulties, there was considerable pressure on the public sector to take an initiative, and provincial governments had limited resources.

Federal cost-sharing the key

Of the individual provinces, Saskatchewan was the only one to start a public hospital insurance scheme on its own, prior to federal cost-sharing. Cost-sharing in this field dates back to the Hospital Insurance and Diagnostic Services Act of 1957, under which the provinces may sign an agreement to establish a hospital insurance program supported by the federal government, with the federal contribution being approximately one-half the total cost (the contribution is a little more than fifty per cent in those provinces where the provincial per capita cost of the program is below the national average, and less than fifty per cent in the others). Legislation which led to the introduction of *comprehensive* health insurance (i.e., including coverage of all treatment by physicians) in all provinces during 1968 to 1971, was passed in December 1966 in the form of the Medical Care Act, under which the federal government agreed to pay half the cost of eligible Medicare programs.

Federal strings attached to Medicare

The federal government cost-sharing came with some strings attached, however. In order to qualify for cost-sharing, the provinces have had to agree to abide by certain conditions governing the insurance programs.[19] These conditions have been similar in several respects for hospital insurance and Medicare, and involve four basic points: 1) The plans must be comprehensive, i.e., cover all types of hospital or physician services which are "medically required", with no exclusions or dollar limits. 2) They must be universally available to all eligible residents on equal terms and conditions. This excludes discrimination in premiums, if premium financing is used, between individuals according to "risk", though exemption from premium payments can be granted to low-income groups, as Ontario does. The conditions do permit "utilization charges", but only if they do not "impede...reasonable access to necessary medical care, particularly for low-income groups," whatever that statement may mean. In practice, it has meant that only few provinces use such charges,[20] and when they are used they are quite low, (for example, B.C. has a $1/day hospital inpatient charge, and a $2.00/visit outpatient fee; between 1968 and 1971, Saskatchewan had a $2.50/visit physician fee and a $2.50/day hospital charge). No plan, however, has any explicit deductibles or co-insurance provisions. 3) The plans must in effect be portable between provinces (i.e., an Ontario resident on a trip to Alberta can get his treatment in Alberta but have it paid for by the Ontario program). 4) The Medicare plans had to be run on a non-profit basis and managed by a public agency accountable to the provincial government. While this does not explicitly rule out the possibility that the plan may be administered by a private carrier or carriers (as was the case in Ontario for several years after its entry into Medicare in 1969), in practice all provinces now administer both their hospital and Medicare plans through public agencies. The fact that the plans have to be comprehensive and that they have been heavily, if not entirely, subsidized by tax financing, plus the fact that the provinces have chosen to administer them publicly, has meant that private health insurance (except for dental services) has been virtually eliminated in Canada. (There are minor exceptions, as evidenced by the forlorn television advertising warning against the disaster about to befall him who is not insured against the cost of dentures or prescription eyeglasses).

With the exception of Quebec (which has had a separate arrangement for its hospital insurance scheme since 1965), by 1971 every province in Canada had agreed to those terms for both hospital insurance and Medicare, so that comprehensive public health insurance was available on the terms prescribed by the agreement, to every Canadian.

Provisions 1) and 2) above are clearly intended to deal with the problem of ''equality of access'' to health care, particularly for low-income groups and individuals who, for one reason or another, are ''bad risks''. They do not, however, in general rule out the possibility of ''opting out'', and Alberta and Ontario continue to permit opting out for specified individuals[21]. Especially where premium financing is used to a substantial extent, as in Ontario, this means that some people will find it worthwhile to opt out (or, more realistically, may not find it worthwhile to opt in, since enrollment is not automatic), so that there still exists a small group of people in Canada who are unprotected by health insurance. It is a very small one, however, partly because in those provinces where premium financing is used, low-income individuals are exempt and have automatic coverage.

Universality of coverage
To what extent then, can the Canadian system be said to have ''solved'' the problem of equality of access, in comparison to the U.K. and the U.S.? Consider first the issue of universality of coverage. Strictly speaking, one cannot say that the Canadian system has achieved universal coverage (as the U.K. system has), because there still are some persons who are not protected by insurance. But it seems pretty clear that more than 99 per cent

have coverage; in the U.S., an estimated 5 per cent have no coverage at all. The more important difference in comparison with the U.S., however, relates not to the universality of protection but rather to comprehensiveness: if you are covered in Canada, you are covered for almost everything. The only exceptions which remain are dental care and the cost of drugs which still have to be paid for by the individual, and the cost of treatment at some extended-care and rehabilitation hospitals, as well as nursing home care in most provinces, but there are no deductibles, co-insurance provisions, or upper limits on the cost of covered services. As long as there are some services which are not included, coverage cannot, of course, be described as completely comprehensive, and to some older persons in Canada whose entire life savings have been wiped out by the cost of long-term treatment in an extended-care hospital or a nursing home, the exclusion of these costs must certainly seem like a significant gap. In spite of this, however, if one defines the problem of equality of access in terms of degrees of universality and comprehensiveness, Canada on the whole comes about as close as the U.K. to having "solved" it, and certainly much closer than the U.S. It is another matter that this may not be a very useful definition of equality of access (for example, it does not consider the quality of the services to which you have access), or that a complete solution to this problem is the wrong goal to work towards (because it completely removes financial responsibility from the consumer of health services). But to me at least, the approach to solving the problem in Canada very closely parallels the non-market approach in the U.K. and bears little resemblance to the modified market approach taken in U.S.

C. THE SUPPLY OF HEALTH SERVICES IN CANADA

i. Hospital services

Under existing programs of hospitalization insurance, hospital services are reimbursed through an approved budget which is based on the actual cost experience of the hospital or the maximum allowable cost.[22] Reimbursement is made not on the basis of charges for different services rendered to individual patients (as in the U.S. system) but rather on the basis of aggregative estimates of the cost of operating the various departments or service units which the hospital has. Under this arrangement, hospitals are guaranteed that they will have enough money to meet operating costs, but approval from the paying authority is required for the addition of new services. Under existing systems, budgeted funds which are not used, revert to the paying authority.

The allocation of hospital resources: political influence

Thus, while hospitals in Canada have not been nationalized but are still "owned" by communities or local groups of individuals, resource allocation decisions ultimately are in the hands of the paying authority. As is well known, some provincial ministries have made energetic attempts in the last few years to slow down the increase in the cost of the hospital systems. These attempts have taken the form of proposals to close some of the smaller, high-cost hospitals, and of strict limitations on expenditures for expansion or the addition of new services and equipment at others, as well as general pressure on hospital managers to keep down the rate of increase in operating costs. The effectiveness of the provincial governments in controlling operating costs through general pressure on hospital managers is probably reduced by the absence of direct financial incentives: an efficient manager will presumably receive an encouraging pat on the head, and may be indirectly rewarded by having his requests for expansion or additional equipment treated with more favour than a less efficient one, but he has no *guarantee* that the money he saves will in fact revert to his hospital. Conversely, less efficient managers or managers of hospitals which are inherently uneconomical because of location or small scale of operations, may not be compelled to cut back if they can convince the ministry that their case merits special consideration for one reason or another. Under those circumstances, it is unavoidable that many decisions by the ministry will be heavily influenced by political factors, as was amply demonstrated in the recent cases of proposals to close a number of small hospitals in Southwestern Ontario.

A further reason why it has been difficult for individual hospitals to control their operating costs has been the centralization of the wage negotiations for hospital workers. These negotiations now take place on a province-wide scale between the government and the provincial union, and since the largest component of operating costs is the wage bill, the rate of increase of operating costs is to a substantial extent outside the influence of the individual hospital.

Market forces have negligible effect

Hence, the role of the market mechanism in allocating resources to meet a given demand for hospital services, is not very great. Neither does the market play much of a part in determining the quantity of services to be performed: as has been previously argued, the cost of a service becomes an irrelevant factor in the doctor's and patient's decision to seek hospital treatment when the patient is fully insured. Since the insurance agencies in Canada do not concern themselves with the cost of particular services rendered to individual patients, but rather try to put a break on rising hospital costs through their control over the overall budget, the hospitals in Canada do not even attempt to estimate the cost by individual service or establish a fee schedule, so that the real costs of different types of procedures may not even be known to the doctors or patients.

ii. Physician services

While some doctors are employed by the hospitals or community health centres and work for a salary (about one-third of the total), most physician services in Canada continue to be provided on a fee-for-service basis.[23] Contrary to the general principle of physician fee setting in the U.S., i.e., that each doctor is free to determine his own fees and bills his patients directly, the practice

in Canada among the vast majority of physicians is to bill the
provincial insurance agency directly for each service, with the
level of the fee being taken from the established fee schedule of
the provincial medical association. In some provinces (notably
Quebec, Ontario, and B.C.), doctors are still permitted to bill the
patient directly for an amount exceeding the established fee
schedule, and the patient may seek reimbursement from the
insurance plan according to the approved fee schedule. The exact
provisions vary: in Quebec, a doctor has to opt out of the plan if
he wants to bill the patient above the schedule, but in that case the
patient will not be reimbursed by the plan; in B.C., a physician
requires the patient's written consent if he wishes to bill
directly.[24] In any event, direct billing is rare even where it is
permitted, and most physicians have chosen the option of
accepting reimbursement from the provincial plan as payment in
full, thereby avoiding the cost of billing and collecting from their
patients.

The determination of medical fee schedules

How are the medical association fee schedules determined?
Clearly, demand factors have no role to play: with universal
health insurance and an unrestricted right for patients to choose
their own doctor, the fee plays no role in the patient's choice of
family doctor or specialist, or in the family doctor's decision
what specialist treatment to recommend. The fees are rather set
by bargaining between the paying agency and the providers; the
institutional mechanism consists of periodic negotiations between the provincial medical association and the agency (which,
in effect, represents the provincial government). In principle,
this negotiation is supposed to produce agreement only on the
average fee level, with the medical association having freedom to
adjust individual service fees subject to the overall agreement,
but in practice, the bargaining process has involved individual
items on fee schedules.

Given the schedules determined in this way, individual
physicians remain free to determine their hours of work, and

where they will locate. Thus in a sense one can still talk about a market for physician services: the location and quantity of services are still determined by independent doctors/suppliers. But the prices of the services do not *directly* respond to supply and demand considerations: the prices to the consumer are effectively zero, and the prices paid to the suppliers are negotiated between the government and organized medicine.

Do medical fees respond to supply and demand?

The next question which arises is now whether the *negotiated* fee schedule responds to supply-demand inbalances: in other words, is there a tendency for this schedule to be established at the level at which the number of doctors and the number of hours they work will be just enough to meet the demand of the patients covered under the provincial plans? Judging from the published statements of the negotiating parties, the answer appears to be no: fee negotiations do not seem to primarily concern the question whether the fee level is adequate to provide the medical services required, but rather whether it provides enough income for doctors to maintain their income level relative to the rest of the population. An increase in the number of doctors, if it tends to decrease the number of patients per doctor (such as has taken place in Canada in the 1960s and 1970s) may then have the opposite effect, i.e., to produce a tendency to raise fees in order to protect doctors' incomes.

Another alternative which was discussed in Chapter One, and which many people feel may have considerable relevance to the Canadian scene, is that a doctor has a good deal of opportunity to influence the quantity of his services that each patient consumes, and may use this influence to protect his income when the number of patients per doctor declines. He may increase the frequency of return visits for follow-up treatment, may recommend surgery of limited or no value to the patient, increase the number of diagnostic tests per patient for infrequent conditions, etc. For all these reasons, few people have much confidence in any tendency for the fee structure, or the level of doctors' incomes, to respond to changes in the supply of doctors in the Canadian system.

Doctor density and doctor incomes

There is some empirical evidence to support this skepticism. If one looks at published data on the incomes of doctors by Canadian province, one finds essentially no relation between income and the number of physicians per capita; in fact, the data indicate a slight *positive* relationship, i.e., the fewer the number of patients per doctor, the *higher* are physician incomes.†[25] The persistent difficulties that some provinces have had in attracting physicians to outlying areas, even through monetary incentives, provide further evidence that doctors are able to earn good incomes even where there are fewer patients for each.

Doctor density and elective surgery

Direct evidence on the extent to which physicians create a demand for their own services is difficult to come by, but the following table which refers to certain types of "elective surgery" requiring hospitalization, is suggestive. It was derived by correlating data on various so-called "elective" surgical procedures, by sex, with the number of doctors and the number of old people (of the corresponding sex), all per 100,000; the data came from two years of observations in each Canadian province.[26] Column 1 in Table 1 gives the "elasticity" of the respective surgical procedures with respect to the number of doctors: thus, for gall bladder operations on males, for example, the results indicate that a 1 per cent increase in the number of physicians in a given province will on the average lead to a 1.06 per cent increase in the rate of such surgery in that province. Column 2 lists for the benefit of the technically inclined reader, the t-ratios corresponding to the physician/population ratio in the regression equations. In the statistician's jargon, more than half of the equations indicate a "statistically significant" positive relationship between surgery rates and the number of physicians, using a 5 per cent one-tailed test, with some being sharply significant. In 23 out of the 28 cases, the partial correlation is positive.

---

† Author's Note: The technically inclined reader may be interested in our regression equation: it was

$$RY = 42,003 + 32.6 \text{ PHCAP} + 1.3 \text{ OLD}, R^2 = .17 \quad ,$$

where RY are physician incomes in the 10 Canadian provinces, 1968-1973, divided by the Canadian consumer price index in each year, PHCAP is the number of physicians per 100,000 people in the corresponding province and year, and OLD is the number of people 65 years of age and older, also per 100,000 people.

Table 1
ELASTICITIES OF RATES OF SURGICAL PROCEDURES
WITH RESPECT TO PHYSICIANS PER CAPITA
(Canadian Data, 1973 and 1974)

ICDA No.	Operation	Sex	Elasticity	t-Statistic
14	Lens and Vitreous	M F	1.08 0.84	5.65 5.15
17	Middle Ear	M F	0.75 (0.50)	1.83 1.42
19	Nose and Accessory Sinuses	M F	0.72 1.15	2.33 2.74
21	Pharynx, Tonsils, and Adenoids	M F	(-0.13) (-0.24)	-0.61 -1.18
244	Excision and Ligation of Varicose Veins	M F	(0.04) (-0.38)	0.10 -1.02
38	Repair of Hernia	M F	0.48 0.51	2.87 2.18
411	Appendectomy	M F	(-0.08) (-0.19)	0.70 -0.08
435	Cholecystectomy (Gall Bladder)	M F	1.06 (0.26)	3.37 1.06
46	Stomach	M F	(-0.22) (0.16)	-1.50 0.77
513	Hemorrhoidectomy	M F	0.90 (0.58)	3.02 1.53
58	Prostate, Seminal Vesicles	M	1.41	5.20
68	Fallopian Tubes	F	0.44	1.84
69	Hysterectomy	F	(0.33)	1.36
714	Plastic Repair: Cystocele and/or Rectocele	F	(0.77)	1.43
86	Incision and Excision of Joint Structures	M F	1.30 0.98	3.17 1.99
87	Other Operations on Joint Structures	M F	0.92 0.88	2.39 2.61

Sources: see Note 26.
Notes: a) The critical Student's t-value for a one-tailed test at a 5% significance
level is 1.74.

b) Elasticities in parentheses are not statistically different from zero.

Like any piece of statistical analysis the results of this one can be interpreted in more than one way (e.g., one might argue that the numbers point to high rates of "untreated disease" in the provinces with few doctors), and do not provide conclusive "proof" of a causal relationship. But again, they certainly are consistent with the notion that under present institutional arrangements, supply and demand factors do not play a major role in determining doctors' income or choice of location: when the number of doctors in a province increases, there apparently will be more things for them to do.

The role of organized medicine in Canada has been similar to that in the U.S. in many respects: the functions of "quality control" and general supervision of the standards of the profession of course are the same. The provincial associations in Canada have also been heavily involved with the public sector through their fee schedule negotiations, so that in this sense organized medicine has had an even more important political role than in the U.S. It does not appear to have had as much influence on the training of new doctors as in the U.S., and as noted above the admissions to medical schools and the training of new physicians in Canada have expanded rapidly; a large part of the expansion, however, in the supply of doctors has taken place through immigration, which essentially has been controlled by federal government policy.

Health Services Organizations

While it does remain true that by far the largest part of physician services in Canada are supplied on a fee-for-service basis, mention should be made of the so-called health services organizations (HSOs) which now operate on an experimental basis in a number of provinces[27] (including Ontario, Saskatchewan, Alberta, B.C., and also in Quebec where legislation now exists which allows voluntary formation of HSOs by groups of doctors). While the precise organization of HSOs varies from case to case, the common feature is that their doctors are not paid on a fee-for-service basis: some are salaried, others are paid capitation fees.

Experimentation with HSOs or "community health centres" was started in 1974, partly as a result of recommendations made in official inquiries (notably the so-called Hastings

103

report of 1972) into the organization of the Canadian health services system.[28] These experiments have several objectives: to investigate the efficiency of providing services by teams of specialist physicians operating in group practice; to consider the potential for higher rates of utilization of paraprofessional services by groups of GPs operating together; to investigate the possibility of combining the supply of health and social services in a single organization (5 or 6 of the 29 HSOs in Ontario provide both); and finally, to establish any effects on patient well-being and on total health care system costs of the increased incentives for preventive care and the reduced incentives for use of hospital facilities which are inherent in a system of capitation reimbursement.

While the original motivation for this kind of experiment probably was derived as much from the organizational reform debate in the British NHS in the early 1970s as from a desire to investigate the possible cost savings of introducing health care delivery along the lines of the Health Maintenance Organizations in the U.S., it is interesting to note that the latter motive is now becoming more important. At the present time, the financial incentives facing doctors and patients in Canadian HSOs are different in two important respects from those in a full-fledged HMO. First, while it may be true that HSO doctors have had no personal financial interest in sending their patients to hospital, the HSOs have not been responsible for the cost of their patients' hospital treatment and hence may not have put the same pressure on their doctors to actively avoid hospitalization as they would have done if, like the HMOs, they *had* been responsible for those costs. Second, patients do not benefit from any cost savings stemming from their enrollment in the HSO; in fact, many patients may not even be aware that they are treated by doctors who are reimbursed on a capitation basis. According to information from the Ontario Ministry of Health, however, there is now discussion of possible incentive schemes whereby HSOs will in effect be financially rewarded for contributing to lower hospitalization costs for their patients, and where patients will be told that the HSO will be financially responsible for health care costs that they incur outside of the HSO.

The quantitative importance of the experimental HSOs has not yet been very great, relatively speaking. In Ontario, for

xample, the 29 HSOs involve no more than 113 doctors and
bout 140,000 enrolled patients. Nevertheless, the results of the
valuations which are now being undertaken should provide a
reat deal of interesting information, and the HSOs may be a
gnificant phenomenon in the sense of indicating a possible
irection for future reform of the system of health care services
ovision in Canada; we will come back to this issue in Chapter
hree.

Who makes the decisions?

\s is clear from the discussion in this section, the central
lecision-making agency in the Canadian health care system is not
he "impersonal market" but rather the provincial government,
through its insurance agency or directly through the provincial
Ministry of Health: they control the hospital budgets and
negotiate about the total pie to be shared among the doctors.
Thus, the system resembles the U.K. one in the sense that the
ultimate decisions affecting the resources used and the cost of the
system, are political ones. From an administrative point of view,
however, the Canadian system is more decentralized because of
the provincial autonomy, even though part of the cost is paid by
the federal government under the cost-sharing arrangements.

As in the U.K., the internal workings of this administrative
system have faced difficulties. Until this year, federal-provincial
cost-sharing was essentially based on the matching principle: for
every dollar of provincial expenditure, the federal government
paid a dollar to the province. This was sometimes described as a
situation where provincial decision-makers were spending
50-cent dollars, and it clearly did not provide the provinces with
very strong incentives to hold back on spending: where else than
in health and education could you offer your citizens a dollar's
worth of services for 50 cents?† Furthermore, the cost-sharing
arrangements were implicitly restrictive by only applying to
hospitals, on the one hand, and *physician* health services, on the
other. With rising costs, the provinces and the federal government have become interested in finding less costly substitutes for
these services, for example nursing home care instead of

---

† Editor's Note: Cost-sharing is discussed at length in *Canadian Confederation at the Crossroads; the Search for a Federal-Provincial Balance,* The
Fraser Institute, 1978; in particular see the paper by Perrin Lewis.

hospitalization for the aged, and paramedics instead of physicians for particular types of services. Since these have not been included in the cost-sharing agreements, the provinces have not had much of an incentive to seriously try to encourage such substitutions by including these services in the provincial plans: had they done so, they would have had to cover the entire cost themselves. In recognition of the fact that this was not a system conducive to economy, the possibility of modifying the cost-sharing agreements has long been under debate between the provinces and the federal government, and since 1977, a new system has been adopted whereby cost-sharing in its present form is eliminated and replaced by a system of per capita grants which the provincial governments may spend as they see fit as long as it does not make the plans violate the basic conditions for federal cost-sharing which were discussed above. This modification, which also applied to cost-sharing in education, certainly represents a step in the right direction, since it gives the provincial government decision-makers an incentive to concentrate more efforts on preventive health and less expensive forms of care rather than on the increasingly costly hospital and physician services, without thereby losing the advantage of federal contributions. The significance of the cost-savings that can be achieved in this way, however, remains to be determined.

iii. A summary of the main elements in the Canadian health care system

I now turn to a brief summary of the institutional organization of the Canadian health services system as outlined above, with particular reference to the question how it compares with the U.S. and U.K. systems.

First of all, the main difference between the U.S. and the Canadian systems lies in the fact that the problem of equality of access without regard to economic factors has essentially been resolved in Canada. Whereas some of the types of services which are covered in the U.K. (such as dentistry, drugs, eyeglasses, and extended care) are still excluded in Canada, the Canadian system in this respect more closely resembles the NHS, with "needed" medical care of almost any kind being available to anybody at no out-of-pocket cost and with no upper limits, and with services being tax-financed to a substantial extent. As in the U.K. also, the fact that individual consumers no longer need to take financial considerations into account when they make their health services consumption decisions has given rise to the need for somebody else to assume the financial responsibility. In Canada, we have only begun to widely recognize this in the last few years, however, and the question exactly how the political control over the system will be exercised, is far from being settled.

On the hospital services side, the Canadian system is similar to the U.S. one only because Canadian hospitals have not been formally nationalized. The method through which hospitals are reimbursed for their services in Canada, however, much more closely resembles the U.K. system: no charges are made for individual services, and hospitals obtain their revenue more or less directly from the public sector through a process of budget submissions to the government authorities. Even though the administrative procedures may differ in details, the basic principle is the same as in the U.K.

Both the system of supply of physician services, and the financial incentives facing physicians in Canada, as in the U.S., are based on the fee-for-service principle and differ sharply from the U.K. system where most doctors (excluding GPs) are paid by salary, and GPs are paid a combination of salary and capitation. The presence of universal, comprehensive and tax-financed health insurance in Canada, however, has meant that the elements preserving some degree of competition in the U.S. market (i.e., competition for patients who are without insurance, or who have deductibles and co-insurance provisions) have been eliminated in Canada. Furthermore, there has been little or no incentive for physicians to join or establish prepayment plans. The institutional arrangements in the Canadian system therefore have tended to weaken spontaneous competition through fees; instead, the fee schedules have come to be established essentially through a bargaining process between organized medicine and the public sector. The political elements would appear to have clearly dominated supply-demand considerations in this process, and unless the system is changed, this trend is likely to continue.

What's left of the market?

Returning to the quote from Bennett and Krasny with which I began this discussion, is it indeed true that the market mechanism plays a major role in determining how resources are allocated in the Canadian health services sector? It seems to me that the answer must be in the negative. Both with respect to health insurance, and in the provision of hospital and physician services, the main determinant of resource allocation is provincial government policy, directly or indirectly. To characterize this system as one in which "resource distribution has been largely determined by market forces" is not useful, in my view. It rather detracts attention from the fact that within the present publicly administered system, the problems to be solved (such as how to pay the doctor, or how to set hospital budgets, or how to organize federal contributions) are administrative problems, the solutions to which have little to do with an ideological commitment or otherwise to the market system. On the other hand, it leads the debate away from the question how well the system would function if we were to reform it such that it *did* rely on the market mechanism in a significant way.

V. PERFORMANCE OF THE SYSTEMS

A. INTRODUCTION: THE KEY QUESTIONS

Against the background of the preceding sections' descriptions of the organization of the health services systems in the U.K., the U.S., and Canada, I now turn to a discussion of the second set of questions outlined in the beginning of this chapter, namely those relating to the efficiency with which the respective systems have performed the functions that they are supposed to perform. In other words, given the amounts of resources used on health services, has the system produced as much output as possible; or conversely, given the output, has it been produced at the least possible cost, i.e., with the use of as little resources as possible? Secondly, has the system been flexible enough to provide individuals with the amount of services they want, given the cost, or is there evidence that institutional rigidities have caused too little output (or too much, for that matter) to be produced?

The problem of measurement

To begin to address these issues, one first of all has to find quantitative measures of inputs and outputs. On the input side, relatively detailed and fairly accurate measures are available, and I will discuss the evidence on resource use and cost in later sections. The definition of the "output" of a health services system, on the other hand, presents considerable difficulty. As I discussed in Chapter One, the fundamental reasons why people are willing to spend money on health services is that they desire long life and good health. To this, perhaps, should be added that many people also put a value on periodic reassurance that they can indeed look forward to, with a high probability, a long life and continued good health. Now, it is reasonably easy to measure the system's ability to produce long life, and we will be discussing some data on this aspect of system performance below. But how does one go about measuring "good health" and "reassurance", and how do we go about adding up mortality reductions and reductions in the incidence of pain and disability in order to get an overall comprehensive measure of the "output" of the health services system?

The recent work on "health indicators" or "health status indices" is an attempt to give an answer to these questions. An interesting example is a recent proposal emanating from the OECD social indicator programme,[29] where it is suggested that indices be computed based on the following factors: *A)* Length of life and healthfulness of life, measured by life expectancy at ages 1, 20, 40, 60; perinatal mortality; proportion of predicted future life to be spent in a state of disability, at ages 1, 20, 40, 60; proportion of persons disabled as a result of permanent impairment in selected age brackets. *B)* Quality of health care in reducing pain and restoring functional capabilities, to be measured by maternal mortality; average delay between an emergency or the awareness of a condition and appropriate treatment; and economic accessibility.

While there are obvious problems with such indicators, in particular that of choosing the weights with which the different factors are supposed to enter, they clearly have the advantage of at least providing a more comprehensive measure of that aspect of human welfare which health services are intended to affect, than do existing partial measures.

Health care or life style the cause?
But unfortunately, the empirical problems do not end even with such a measure. Suppose we had a set of health indicators for a group of different societies. We would still be faced with the problem of deciding whether variations in those numbers should be ascribed to the performance of the health services system or to other factors such as life style, environment, or income. Suppose we find a healthy population with a big health services system. Does that mean that the system is producing good health, or are they wasting money on health services even though they are basically healthy? Or suppose we find an unhealthy population with a big system. Does that mean that the system is inefficient, or does it mean that it has to be big because the population tends to be unhealthy? In practice, the problem is further complicated because we do not in fact have many data on the health of the population (apart from mortality data); rather we have mostly measurements of the consumption of health services (number of visits to the doctor, hospital days per capita, etc.). Those measures tell us something about treated disease, but not about how much disease goes untreated. So we have the same sort of problem again: a low rate of services consumption may mean that the population is healthy (because of absence of poverty, healthy life-style and environment, or an effective preventative system) or that many sick persons do not receive treatment. Finally, how does one measure "reassurance", or the satisfaction to be derived by the patient from a good relationship with his doctor? For example, we may have two populations with the same mortality risks and of "equal health", but with one population being better off because they have easier access to doctors and hospitals for diagnostic services, or they have freedom to choose their own doctor or consult with several doctors, or they can be assured of dealing with their own personal physician rather than being assigned a different doctor every time they seek treatment. Casual evidence indicates that people do attach value to these things; but we don't know how much.

No unambiguous measures of output
So the sad fact is that in the health services field, we do not have unambiguous output measures which can be compared with the cost of a system in order to get a global comparison of its

efficiency relative to alternative ones. Nevertheless, the incomplete data that are available will be more consistent with some hypotheses regarding relative efficiency than with others, and it is useful to discuss them as long as it is borne in mind that the evidence is indirect and suggestive rather than direct and conclusive, for purposes of efficiency comparisons.

B. MORTALITY AND LIFE EXPECTANCY INDICATORS OF PERFORMANCE

Canada ranks first

As observed above, the most accurate data bearing on the success of a health services system are those on mortality. The broadest measure available is "life expectancy at birth", defined as the average future lifetime of a person subject to age-specific death rates pertaining to a given population at a given time; it therefore constitutes an index which varies inversely with the levels of age-specific death rates. As is seen in Table 2, Canada in 1972 had a somewhat higher life expectancy for both males and females than either the U.K. or the U.S., but the differences are small. While Canada was doing better than both countries in 1961 as well, she then had a lower value for both males and females, than the U.K. had in 1972, about the same value for males as the U.S. white male figure in 1972, and lower than the U.S. 1972 figure for white females.

Table 2
LIFE EXPECTANCY AT BIRTH (Years)

| | 1951 | | 1961 | | 1972 | |
	M	F	M	F	M	F
Canada	66.3	70.8	68.4	74.2	69.3	76.7
U.K.	66.2	71.2	68.1	74.0	68.8	75.1
U.S., White	66.5*	72.2*	67.4*	74.1*	68.3	75.9
U.S., Negro and Other	59.1*	62.9*	61.1*	66.3*	61.5	66.9

*U.S. figures are for 1950 and 1960, respectively.
Sources: see Note 30.

The first point that strikes one as surprising in this table is how close the numbers are at each given time: as was noted briefly in Chapter One, the U.K. appears to devote a much smaller amount of resources to health services, on a per capita basis, than either the U.S. or Canada, yet life expectancy at birth in the U.K. is about the same as in the U.S. If one abstracts from infant mortality and considers life expectancy at age 1, the rankings are much the same: of the three countries, Canada ranks first, followed by the U.K. and the U.S. in that order. It is interesting to note that with this criterion, European countries such as Italy, Spain and Portugal also had longer life expectancies than the U.S.[31] There are several interpretations for this: either that for this comparatively rich group of countries (by international standards), neither income level nor health care resources have much of an effect on life expectancy, or else that they have offsetting effects: the life styles and environment in the highest income countries, such as the U.S. and Canada, tend to decrease life expectancy, and a large amount of health care resources are spent on counteracting this effect.

The effects of life style
While the evidence is not strong, some confirmation of the hypothesis that life style related mortality plays a role in explaining the relatively unfavourable position for the U.S., can be had as follows. If one assumes that this factor should have relatively more importance in influencing the death rates of those who are neither very young nor very old, one would expect that the mortality differences, at least when comparing U.S. whites with the populations of the U.K. or Canada, should be smaller for the younger and older groups than for those in between. There is some evidence that this is indeed the case: U.S. white infant mortality rates in the early 1970s were no higher than those in Canada or the U.K. (if anything, they were a little bit lower), and life expectancies (male and female) at age 65 were higher in the U.S. than in the U.K. and were closer to the Canadian figures than were the life expectancies at age 50.

It may also be of some interest to briefly consider how mortality has changed over time in the respective systems. Here it turns out that the largest increase in life expectancy since 1951 has occurred in Canada, the smallest in the U.S. (Note, however, that U.S. whites had the longest life expectancy at birth of all three countries in 1951). Most of the Canadian improvement has occurred through a rapid decline in infant mortality, which in

1951 was considerably higher in Canada than in the U.K. or in the U.S. white population as Table 3 shows.

Table 3
INFANT MORTALITY
(Deaths per 1,000 live births)

	1951		1961		1974	
	M	**F**	**M**	**F**	**M**	**F**
Canada	42.7	34.0	30.5	23.7	16.6	13.4
U.K.	35.1	26.9	24.5	19.6	18.9	14.4
U.S., White	30.7	23.6	25.9	19.6	16.8	12.9
U.S., Non-White	50.9	40.9	47.0	38.3	27.3	22.4

Sources: see Note 32.

Conclusions from aggregative mortality statistics

The general conclusion from these data must be that aggregative mortality statistics do not provide much of a criterion for comparing the efficiency of the health services system. Whereas it is suggested that even U.S. whites have life expectancies shorter than those of Canadians or U.K. residents, this appears to be at least partially attributable to life style phenomena: those mortality rates that one can expect to be most influenced by health services appear to be fairly close together in all three countries. With respect to infant mortality, the fact that the U.K. rates are relatively close to the North American ones is the more remarkable as hospitalization and the use of physician services are used to a much smaller extent in connection with childbirth in the U.K. Typically,women are hospitalized only when they are about to have their first baby, and subsequently not until the fourth one; the second and third babies are generally delivered at home by a midwife, and antenatal and postnatal care is typically given by paramedical personnel rather than by doctors. On the other hand, the wide discrepancy between the white and non-white mortality experience in the U.S. can be taken as consistent with the idea that the inequality of access to the U.S. health care system raises mortality in the disadvantaged groups, but it is impossible to decide to what extent the difference is due to life style and environment factors as well.

113

Evidence from the causes of mortality

If one considers the statistics on mortality by cause, the picture is much the same. As is well known, in the industrialized countries of the world, the large-scale killers of an earlier era, i.e., infectious and parasitic diseases (such as influenza, tuberculosis, intestinal diseases) have been replaced by the so-called degenerative diseases as the leading causes of death. As seen from Table 4, the relative weights of the two leading causes of death, heart disease and cancer, are about the same in the three countries, with heart disease accounting for roughly half of all deaths, and cancer for about one fifth, in each. Violent death (i.e., accidents, suicide and homicide, etc.) is the third leading cause of death in Canada and the U.S. which both have more than twice as high a rate as the U.K. While the quality and access to the health services system may of course have a major impact on the mortality in accidents, etc., it is clearly overshadowed by other factors, especially speed and frequency of passenger vehicle travel. In the U.K. the proportion of deaths attributable to diseases of the respiratory system (primarily pneumonia and bronchitis) is more than twice as high as in the U.S. or Canada; medical men will tell you, however, that cigarette smoking, air pollution, and a maritime climate are major influences on this rate, so that it is not clear that the difference can be attributed to the health care system.

Table 4
DEATHS BY MAJOR CATEGORY, 1974
(% of all deaths)

	U.S.	U.K.	Canada
Cardiovascular, Renal	52.2	51.8	49.5
Malignant Neoplasms	18.6	20.8	20.2
Respiratory System	4.1	13.3	6.5
Accidents, Suicide, Homicide	7.8	3.9	10.1

Sources: see Note 33.

The evidence, again, is difficult to interpret but is consistent with the hypothesis that the health services systems are approximately equal in their effectiveness at reducing overall mortality, or at least that any difference between them is overshadowed by the influence of life style and environmental factors. One would not expect, however, that this would be equally true for all causes of mortality; thus, a better comparison might be made if one could study differences in mortality due to causes where life style and environment differences were of relatively less importance, and where medical intervention could be shown to be relatively effective. Without extensive medical expertise, it is not easy to isolate such cases, but we did make a crude attempt, as follows. From North American mortality statistics, we found a number of disease categories for which mortality had decreased substantially since the early 1950s, and where there was no obvious reason to attribute these declines to life style, environmental or demographic factors. Comparing the death rates from these causes between the U.S., U.K., and Canada in the early 1970s would then give an indication, albeit a partial one, of the relative progress that had been made in utilizing medical technology which was known to be effective at reducing these forms of mortality. The comparison is given in Table 5.

Table 5
DEATHS BY SELECTED CAUSES
(% of all deaths, mid-1970s)

	U.S.	U.K.	Canada
Rheumatic Fever, Rheumatic Heart Disease	.69	1.01	.71
Hypertension, Hypertensive Heart Disease	.98	1.41	.90
Peptic Ulcer, Hernia and Intestinal Obstruction	.70	1.14	.87
Nephritis, Nephrosis	.42	.50	.34
Infective and Parasitic Diseases	.63	.55	.67
Congenital Anomalies	.70	.81	1.03
Causes of Perinatal Mortality	1.49	1.09	1.47

Sources: see Note 34

Clearly, the table must be interpreted with great caution and may even yield a slightly biased picture: the categories chosen were those where North American mortality was known to have

declined significantly; classification systems may differ somewhat and only 6 to 6.5 per cent of all deaths are caused by the
conditions listed. Nevertheless, the table is consistent with the
view that the greater amounts of medical resources in the North
American systems have led to mortality rates below the U.K.
ones for certain conditions where surgery or other treatment may
be particularly beneficial, such as certain types of heart disease,
diseases of the digestive and genito-urinary systems, and for
infants with congenital anomalies. On the other hand, very low
incomes and living standards at the bottom end of the scale as
well as the remaining (and related) inequality of access to medical
care in the U.S. may well have contributed to the relatively higher
death rates from infectious disease and diseases of early infancy
(in comparing the last two lines, however, it should be
remembered that they are influenced by relative birth rates as
well). But, I repeat again, this comparison refers to causes of
death which account for no more than 6 to 6.5 per cent of all
mortality in either country, and should be taken with a good deal
of skepticism given the difficulties of accurate classification of
disease categories.

Conclusions from all mortality data

The broad conclusion from this brief survey of the mortality
patterns in the three systems must thus essentially be an agnostic
one: the differences in overall mortality are relatively small, and
when they exist, they are as compatible with the notion that they
are due to differences in life style and environment (which are
clearly related to income) as they are with the idea that they are
due to differences in the accessibility and effectiveness of the
health care systems. Thus, the cautious and rigorously scientific
conclusion must be that no firm generalizations are possible.
Nevertheless, at the cost of sacrificing some of the caution and
rigour, one may note certain interesting aspects of the evidence
which may warrant the attention of those having to make
decisions about the health care field.

i. Canada has best improvement in life expectancy

Of the three countries, Canada showed the largest increase in life
expectancy between the early 1950s and the early 1970s
primarily due to falling infant mortality. At the same time, th

overall rate of infant mortality in the U.S. remained high because the non-white rate remained high. Both these pieces of evidence are clearly consistent with the hypothesis that the move toward greater equality of access in the Canadian system through universal comprehensive health insurance paid a non-trivial dividend in increasing life expectancy, and that the U.S. might have a similar experience if disadvantaged groups were to make more use of the health services system. The Medicare and Medicaid program may ultimately accomplish this; and programs to increase the incomes of such groups may lead to a spontaneous increase in their health services consumption. But the evidence does seem to me to strengthen the case for some form of guaranteed universal access to health care in cases of serious illness, along the lines of the Canadian system.

ii. Most expenditures in the health services sector are not of the "who shall live" variety

Overall life expectancy and infant mortality in the U.K. are not much different from those in Canada or the U.S. The U.K. has a system which effectively guarantees equality of access to medical care. But it has significantly fewer doctors and lower hospitalization rates than either the U.S. or Canada, and it is much less costly. While the lower cost of health care may partly mean a higher cost in terms of pain and suffering from disease which is not life-threatening (see below), or in part be due to lower costs of inputs into the production of health services (lower salaries for doctors or less expensive hospitals), this evidence also points to the possibility of providing health care at lower cost while continuing to save as many lives as before. In other words, the U.K. experience may be interpreted to mean that there is indeed some real choice in deciding how much money the society is to spend on health care: most expenditure decisions in the health services sector are not of the "who shall live" variety.

iii. Life style and environmental factors very important

It is increasingly clear, both from the cross-country and time series evidence, that a large portion of mortality is due to life style and environment-related causes; this of course is the theme which was strongly emphasized by Marc Lalonde in his recent working document on the health of Canadians.[35] Thus, an increasing proportion of the money which we spend on health care is spent on taking care of the consequences of the behaviour of those who drink, smoke, and eat too much, drive too fast, and sit still all the time, or the consequences of environmental pollution. At the same time, the types of diseases associated with those conditions (heart disease and cancer) are also those where medical intervention with present technology tends to be expensive and of somewhat uncertain effectiveness. This raises several issues. First, as I have just observed, it makes it difficult to compare the effectiveness of health care systems on the basis of mortality data alone. Second, however, it raises the question whether it remains valid to restrict the evaluation of the system's effectiveness to the provision of health services. The most efficient system may not be the one in which many lives are saved in intensive care units, but instead one where people eat, drink, and smoke in moderation, drive slowly and jog fast, and where pollution is well controlled. In any system, it may therefore become increasingly important that individuals (or firms) face the proper incentives in choosing their life styles, or in designing their chemical plants; I will return in Chapter Three to the question whether these incentives can be provided within a market system.

C. PREVENTING DISABILITY AND PAIN

Mortality versus pain and disability
The discussion up to this point has focussed on only one aspect of the outcome of supplying health services, namely that of preventing death. But the possibility of death is of course not the only consequence of ill health. As was noted at the outset, the desire to avoid pain, disability and anxiety about one's health, may be equally important motives in seeking health care. Unfortunately, the data designed to measure such things as differing degrees of disability and pain and their extent are only now beginning to become available, and it is not yet possible to make sensible cross-country comparisons on the basis of direct observation. The limited data that are available, as also noted above, primarily refer to inputs into the production of health: how many hospital days, etc., were devoted to the treatment of people suffering from various conditions? Inferences about the effects

that such inputs might have on pain and disability can only be made if one is willing to make a number of assumptions, some of which are of uncertain validity. Nevertheless, indirect evidence is better than no evidence, and I will attempt to speculate below on the comparative effectiveness of three systems in this respect, using the imperfect information we have.

The degree to which the health care system affects the amount of disability and pain is obviously not independent of its effectiveness at reducing mortality. In part, the relationship will be negative: as medical care reduces mortality it will produce a larger number of disabled survivors. Since, with few exceptions, people prefer life, even with a disability, to death, the net effect on welfare is presumably still positive, but this reasoning draws attention to the fact that one has to be careful in assessing the total effect of reducing mortality. If all that is accomplished by a particular procedure is to prolong life for an individual who will remain disabled and in pain, this procedure is clearly not as valuable to people as one that produces healthy survivors. Evaluation reflecting this kind of consideration is now beginning to creep into resource allocation decisions in the health care area: the measure of ''quality-adjusted'' life-years saved has been proposed as a better measure of the output of a procedure than simply lives saved.[36]

Apart from this kind of effect, however, it is also reasonable to assume that a system that is effective in reducing mortality from given types of diseases (heart disease, say) will also be more likely to reduce the degree of disability and pain for those who do not die: if the technology and the resources are there to reduce mortality, they can also be used to treat patients threatened with disability and pain. But it is of course true that various diseases are quite different in terms of risk of death, and risk of disability and pain. Some may kill you with relatively little pain; others may not, but may give you prolonged pain and disability.

Towards measuring pain and disability reduction
Now consider two health care systems that perform about equally well in reducing mortality, such as the United Kingdom and Canada, say. We cannot get data which bear directly on the question how effective they are at also reducing disability and pain. But suppose we could measure the amount of resources

used in treating different categories of disease, and suppose one found that Canada, say, was using more resources for any given disease; suppose also that one could observe that Canada was using *comparatively* more resources in treating diseases which have relatively low mortality rates. This might of course mean only that the Canadian system is wasteful. But a more plausible explanation would be that in the Canadian system more resources are spent on less "serious" cases or less serious diseases, with the objective of reducing disability and pain, not just saving lives.

We do not, unfortunately, have a good index of the total amount of resources spent on treating different diseases; a partial index, however, can be obtained by looking at hospitalization data. For the United Kingdom, information is available on "selected diagnoses of persons treated in non-psychiatric departments"; for Canada, there are data on "separations" by cause. While the number of persons treated for all causes is slightly larger than the number of "separations" in the United Kingdom, the difference is minor and is unlikely to distort the broad pattern. In comparing the separations figures with mortality by cause and with overall mortality, one does have to bear in mind that in 1973, the year of the comparison, the United Kingdom had a much larger proportion of old people than did Canada; hence, even if the health services systems were equally effective for any given disease, one would expect a higher death rate in the United Kingdom. But with higher mortality among the old, one would also expect a higher separation rate from hospitals. The latter indication, however, is not borne out by the data: in 1974 the United Kingdom had 110 hospital separations per thousand people, with the corresponding figure for Canada being 165. While this difference may be explained by a number of factors, such as more visits to doctors outside of hospitals serving as a substitute for hospitalization in the United Kingdom, or longer average stay for old people, it is hard to believe that the figure does not to some extent reflect the scarcity of hospital facilities in the United Kingdom and hence more people with risk of disability or suffering from pain not receiving treatment. If none of these explanations is true, one must conclude that the Canadian system simply is wasteful!

Table 6 is designed to provide some information about the degree of "seriousness" of diseases treated in U.K. and Canadian hospitals, as follows.

Table 6
HOSPITALIZATION EPISODES/DEATH AND PROPORTION OF HOSPITALIZATION EPISODES
(by selected disease categories, mid-1970s)

	1 U.K.	2 Canada	3 U.K.	4 Canada
Tuberculosis	13.5	12.5	0.4	0.14
Malignant Neoplasms	2.5	4.0	6.1	3.6
Benign Neoplasms	89.3	277.0	2.2	2.1
Endocrine, Metabolic	12.4	18.5	1.8	2.0
Nervous System	13.1	28.4	1.7	1.4
Cardio-Vascular System	1.6	4.5	10.0	9.9
Respiratory System	5.2	43.9	8.5	12.7
Digestive System	33.4	73.5	9.8	12.1
Genito-Urinary System	10.1	79.4	1.6	4.3
Childbirth	*	*	17.9	13.3
Musculo-Skeletal System	66.7	277.0	3.5	4.3
Fractures, Injuries	30.2	35.3	10.6	9.4

*Not computed because of the very small number of maternal deaths in either country.
Sources: see Note 37.

In columns 1 and 2, I have computed the number of hospital separations per death in selected major disease classifications, and for comparison, the proportion of all separations associated with the respective categories in columns 3 and 4. It is seen that, with the single exception of tuberculosis, Canada has a larger number of hospitalization episodes per death for each type of disease. If one looks at low-mortality diseases with over 40 hospitalization episodes per death in Canada, one finds that they account for 35.5 per cent of all episodes in Canada but only for 25.6 per cent of those in the U.K. The major categories in this group are diseases of the respiratory, digestive, genito-urinary and musculo-skeletal systems, all of which can vary greatly in severity ranging from the life-threatening to simply that of a minor irritation. In particular, Canadian hospitalizations for respiratory disease include a very large number attributable to "hypertrophy of tonsils and adenoids" and "unspecified acute upper respiratory infections" (colds). Some of the largest subcategories of musculo-skeletal diseases are arthritis and slipped discs. On the other hand, the high-mortality diseases, i.e., heart disease, strokes, and cancer, account for 13.5 per cent of hospitalization episodes in Canada vs. 16.1 per cent in the U.K. It is noteworthy that even for a high-mortality class of conditions such as cardio-vascular disease, the number of hospitalization episodes relative to the number of deaths apparently is much lower in the U.K. It is difficult to tell whether this represents a statistical aberration, or a difference in the ages of the patients, or whether it represents a real difference in the quality of care for patients with cardio-vascular disease.

U.K. system less effective than Canadian in reducing pain

While the differences in the hospitalization patterns just described are not major, they *are* consistent with the idea that a larger proportion of resources in Canada are spent on treating disease associated with temporary disability and pain only, and hence that the U.K. system is relatively less effective in eliminating those than it is in reducing mortality. One can finally note that there is some direct evidence that this is indeed the case, in the form of the notorious waiting lists to get into hospitals for various forms of treatment, especially for so-called elective surgery. For 1975, the statistics show a waiting list in England and Wales of over 600,000 people.[38] If one takes into account that for some types of treatment (such as childbirth or serious acute conditions) there cannot be any waiting lists, it is apparent that the expected waiting time for those who suffer from diseases where treatment *can* wait, may be very long. Thus, if one recognizes the temporary disability and pain that may be associated with those conditions, the waiting lists do indeed confirm that part of the price of devoting a relatively small amount of resources to health services in Britain is borne by the patients.

Canada compared to U.S.

The above comparisons pertain to Canada and the U.K. only; I have not been able to find comparable disaggregated statistics for the U.S. One suspects that the reason for this is the lesser incentive for system-wide data collection in a highly decentralized system such as the American one. From the aggregative statistics, however, it can be seen that total hospitalization in 1974 was broadly comparable to the rate for Canada, with the rate of admissions being 165 per thousand (i.e., the same as the figure for Canada quoted above). Because the U.S. population is somewhat older, the death rate is higher than the Canadian one (94 vs. 74 per thousand in 1973), and the average number of hospitalization episodes per death is considerably lower than in Canada (17.0 vs. 22.6); both of those are much higher than the comparable average for the U.K. which is 8.0.[39] Neither Canada nor the U.S. have any significant waiting lists for hospital admission; in Canada this presumably reflects the fact that there are sufficient hospital facilities to fill the demand of the entire population when the cost to the patient or the doctor is zero. In the U.S., it merely means that the facilities are adequate to meet the demand from those who are covered by insurance or who can afford to pay out of their own pocket, but even though the average hospitalization rate is about the same as in Canada, it is clearly possible that there are individuals enduring disability and pain who cannot financially afford to seek hospital treatment or do not have insurance. Given the existence of the Medicare and Medicaid program, however, the number of such individuals should not be large, and on the whole, there is no strong evidence to distinguish the performance of the U.S. system from the Canadian one in this respect.

Conclusions from pain and disability data
To summarize the brief discussion of morbidity, one may ask what additional evidence on the relative efficiency of the health services systems can be obtained from morbidity data, beyond the evidence from mortality. The answer is that it is very limited, given the absence of systematic data on the prevalence of disability and pain associated with different diseases, in the respective populations. The only evidence I have been able to find relates to hospital morbidity, and hence excludes both untreated morbidity or treatment by doctors outside of hospitals.

The major conclusion from the hospital morbidity data is that the U.K. system devotes much less resources to treating patients in hospitals than do the North American systems, and that the difference is especially marked in the "less serious" disease categories, i.e., those tending to have low mortality per hospital episode. This is consistent with the hypothesis that there is more untreated disease, and hence a higher incidence of disability and pain, in the U.K. In the discussion of mortality, I raised the suggestion that the U.K. performance in this respect could be interpreted to indicate that there was a lot of "fat" in the North American systems, i.e., that the population could be maintained in good health using considerably fewer resources than they presently do. The evidence discussed here raises the question whether indeed "health" is as good in the U.K. as one would conclude from the mortality data, i.e., whether the mortality data can in fact be taken as an indication of superior efficiency in the U.K. On the one hand, it is possible that the lesser incentive on U.K. doctors to send their patients to hospital, and the cost-cutting efforts of NHS bureaucrats have simply eliminated the kind of fat that perhaps exists in the North American systems, without ill effects on anybody's health. On the other hand, the waiting lines and the apparent existence of untreated "minor" disease may also represent an instance where a rigid but economy-minded bureaucratic system prevents people from getting treatment for which they would in fact be willing to pay the cost if they had the choice. One suspects that many of those who are queuing for hospital admission for elective surgery would subscribe to the latter view. From a Canadian viewpoint, the relevant question is whether we would be willing to pay this kind of a price for letting the bureaucrats decide how and when to save money in the health care sector, rather than making those decisions for ourselves.

VI. RESOURCES AND COSTS
IN THE THREE SYSTEMS

The purpose of the preceding section was to summarize the available evidence on the performance in the three systems in terms of what people get out of the systems. In the following sections, I turn to a discussion of the resource costs: how many hospital beds, doctors, x-ray machines, pills and bandages are used, and at what cost, in order to get this output.

As I noted in Chapter One, the amount of resources spent on the health care systems in the U.S., U.K., and Canada are indeed very large. The data I presented indicate that in 1975, 8.6, 5.6 and 6.9 per cent of GDP was used in the production of health services in the respective countries.[40] In Canada, this corresponded to about $500 for every man, woman and child; the corresponding U.S. figure was $615. Both because of the somewhat smaller share of GDP and the lower per capita income in the U.K., their figure was quite a bit lower, at about $230. How is this difference to be explained?

A. HOSPITAL SERVICES

The three largest categories of health expenditure, in any of the countries, are hospital services, physician services, and drugs, in that order. Considering hospital services first, the Canadian system is the one most well-equipped with hospital beds: in 1974, it is seen to have had an estimated 650 hospital beds per hundred thousand people, with the U.S. having around 500 and the U.K. below that figure (Table 7). In spite of the waiting lists for specific types of minor surgery in the U.K., on the average the occupancy rate in English hospitals is not more than 75 per cent. This is about the same rate as prevails in the U.S. and Canada, so that the number of patient days is roughly proportional to the number of beds.

Canada heaviest user of hospitals

It is noteworthy that Canada uses as much as 31 per cent more hospital days per capita in producing health services than does the U.S. The number of hospitalization episodes (i.e., admissions or separations) in Canada and the U.S. are approximately the same, and are 50 per cent higher than in the U.K. Hence, most of the difference between the number of patient days in the U.S. and Canada is attributed to the longer average length of stay in Canada, estimated here at around eleven and a half days per episode, which is fairly close to the U.K., with the U.S. having a significantly lower figure.

Table 7
HOSPITAL CAPACITY AND UTILIZATION, PER 100,000
General and Allied Hospitals (excluding psychiatric)

	Canada (1974)	U.S. (1974)	U.K. (1974)
Hospital Beds	650	516	491
Number of Episodes	165	165	112
Patient Days	1,872	1,432	1,431
Average Length of Stay (days)	11.3	8.7	12.8

Sources: see Note 41.

Thus, by the patient-day measures, the Canadian health services system is by a substantial margin the heaviest user of hospital services of the three systems, and must rank nearly first in the world in this respect. Especially in comparison with the U.K., this is the more surprising given the age structure of the population. The available data for the Canadian hospital system show that the age groups above 65 have substantially higher hospitalization rates than the younger groups: in 1973, this group had a patient-day use of 8.4 days per person, to be compared with the overall average of 1.9 days per person[42]. As a consequence, this group accounted for about 37 per cent of all patient-days even though they only represent about 8 per cent of the population. Because of different fertility and migration patterns, however, the 65 and over group in the U.K. accounts for 13.6 per cent[43] of the population, i.e., nearly twice the Canadian figure. Therefore, if one were to adjust hospital services consumption for the age distribution, the difference between Canadian (and, to a somewhat lesser extent, U.S.) rates and the U.K. ones would appear even more dramatic than it already is. I will return to the question how to interpret this difference at a later stage. Part of the explanation, presumably, lies in the fact that many babies in the U.K. are delivered at home and not in the hospital. But one might also argue that it is likely to reflect on the one hand, a substitution of non-hospital services for hospitalization in the U.K., and on the other, the possible tendency for "less serious" conditions to go untreated.

As just noted, the difference between Canadian and U.S. rates of hospital services consumption is mainly attributable to a

126

longer average length of stay in Canada. I do not have any direct information with which to explain the difference, but one can speculate on possible causes. First, hospital insurance coverage in the U.S. is not universal, and even those covered by insurance frequently have limits on the amounts or rates to be reimbursed. Hence, many patients have a financial interest in making their stay short, and their doctors may comply. Insurance companies may also put pressure on doctors and hospitals to avoid unnecessarily long stays, by questioning their medical necessity. Second, though I no have direct evidence on this point, it may be true that there is a tendency in the North American systems to hospitalize people for ''tests'' or ''observation'', for minor ''elective'' surgery (tonsillectomies, hernia repairs, hemor-rhoidectomy, etc.) All of these categories require only relatively short stays, so that if they account for a large part of all stays, the average length of stay will fall. While this may explain a good deal of the difference between average lengths of stay in North America and the U.K., it is harder to explain the difference between the U.S. and Canada in those terms.

The unit operating cost per patient-day in public general hospitals in Canada in 1974 was approximately $96; the comparable U.S. figure was about $128.[44] The figure for the U.K. is not available on a comparable basis, but it is clear that it is considerably lower: based on a number of assumptions, including one that the relative cost of a patient-day in a psychiatric department to one in a general hospital is the same as in the U.S., the cost per patient-day in a non-psychiatric department can very roughly be estimated at $55 in 1974.[45] In interpreting the latter amount, it should be remembered that in the U.K., the payments to full-time salaried hospital physicians and part-time consultants are included in the operating costs of hospitals; in the North American systems, where the number of salaried hospital physicians is a much smaller proportion of the total number of doctors, they are mostly included in the total cost of physician services. If the U.K. figure were adjusted for this, it would of course be even lower relative to North America.

To what factors should one attribute this dramatic difference in patient-day cost? Apparently not to differences in total hospital staffing: whatever data are available on hospital manpower (other than physicians) suggest that if anything, the U.K. has a larger full-time hospital system staff per bed than does Canada, and utilization rates for hospital beds are roughly comparable. But the difference in hospital staff wage levels is of course large. While I don't have data which permit a precise comparison, we know that wages in general are lower in the U.K. Consider the following illustrative calculation: suppose wages in Canada in 1974 were twice as high as in the U.K. (this corresponds roughly to the ratio of the corresponding per capita incomes in that year).[46] Suppose also that wages account for 2/3 of total operating costs in both systems. If the British wage levels for hospital staff in 1974 had been 2 times as high as they in fact were, the cost per patient-day would have been $92 instead of $55!

This factor only accounts for part of the difference, however, and does not take into consideration the fact that specialist salaries are included in hospital cost in the U.K., nor of the possibilities that may exist to keep costs down in the North American systems by substituting non-labour services (such as electronic communications systems rather than messengers, devices for mechanized rather than manual record-keeping, or what have you) for the high-priced labour services. Other things equal, the remaining cost differential would thus appear to suggest that North American hospital managers simply have not succeeded in producing patient days efficiently.

But even casual impression suggests that other things aren't equal in the sense that a patient-day does not mean the same thing in the three systems. In particular, the amount and cost of ancillary services per patient day produced by sophisticated and expensive equipment such as coronary care units, intensive care units, dialysis machines, radiology departments, the new "computerized axial tomography" (CAT) diagnostic scanners, etc., etc., must be considerably higher in North America than in the U.K. This impression is also consistent with data on changes in hospital services inputs over time in the U.S. and Canada. It appears that in both systems, *both* manpower *and* other inputs per patient-day have been growing since the mid-1960s, though at a fairly slow rate. Bennett and Krasny state that in Canada the number of hospital workers per day has grown by less than 1 per cent, with non-labour components growing at 6 per cent.[47] In the U.S., data from the 1965 to 1973 period suggest corresponding figures of about 3 per cent and a little less than 10 per cent, respectively.[48] These figures reflect the nature of advances in medical technology: rather than making it possible to produce the same service to the patient with less resources, technological advance appears primarily to raise costs by leading to the use of better and more advanced services, but at a higher cost in terms of resources. Hence, over time, the quality of a patient-day, in terms of services provided, appears to have risen, and this has been one of the explanations, perhaps the main one, for the rapidly rising costs. At the same time, hospital wages for the same periods have risen at an annual rate of 12.5 per cent and 7 per cent in the U.S. and Canada, with non-labour input prices having gone up by 4 to 6 per cent in both countries.[49] Hence, in both cases, the growth in labour, which was becoming relatively more expensive, was considerably slower than the growth of other inputs, as one would expect in a situation where hospital managers attempt to use inputs efficiently.

On the whole, therefore, it is clear that to a significant extent, the difference between hospital systems costs in North America and the U.K. is due to the higher prices of inputs, primarily labour, in the North American systems. While a precise estimate is not possible, it is also clear, however, that differences in the rates of hospital services consumption are quite significant as well. The U.K. has a lower hospitalization rate, in spite of an older population; in addition, and perhaps equally important, the consumption of ancillary services per patient-day appears to be much higher in the North American system. Thus, there is little evidence that North American hospitals are inefficient in the sense of using excessive amounts of resources, given the services they produce. But again, the *system* may tend to be wasteful in the sense of providing too much of these services, or providing them in too many places, given the cost.

B. PHYSICIAN SERVICES

I now turn to the second major category of health care services, namely physician services. In Canada, this component accounts for well over 20 per cent of total health care expenditures, and has been growing rapidly in recent years.

Again, the question of primary interest to us is a comparison between the relative per capita expenditure on, and consumption of, physician services in the U.S., Canada, and the U.K. Considering first the consumption of services, a natural question to ask is whether the lower rate of hospitalization in the U.K. is counterbalanced by a heavier reliance on physician services. In other words, is there a substitution of doctors for hospitals in producing "good health" in the U.K.?

People in U.S. consult physicians most frequently
The tentative answer to this question, based on a simple count of doctors, must be no. There do in fact appear to be fewer physicians per head in the U.K. than in either of the North American systems: estimated numbers per hundred thousand in the population are 105, 141, and 164 in the U.K. (1974), U.S. (1973) and Canada (1974) respectively.[50] In interpreting these figures, it should be noted that the U.K. figure may be a bit of an underestimate, as it includes only physicians either listed on NHS hospital medical staff or registered with the NHS as active general practitioners; hence physicians practicing outside the NHS or those employed in administration or research would not be included. In spite of these qualifications, however, the evidence clearly indicates a substantial difference between the U.K. and the North American systems in the number of doctors.[51] Recent estimates of the numbers of consultations with a doctor per person indicate a similar ranking: they are given as 3.5, 5.0 and 4.61 for the U.K. (1974), U.S. (1974) and Canada (1973).[52] Hence the conclusion seems to be very clear: not only does the U.K. system have a substantially lower hospitalization rate, it also has a substantially lower rate of utilization of physician services than do the North American systems. Again, it should be noted that this difference is the more significant as the U.K. population contains a much larger proportion of older persons than the U.S. or Canadian populations.

Paramedical services more prominent in the U.K.
In part, the U.K. figures probably reflect the same problem as was discussed in the case of hospital services, i.e., people with relatively "minor" ailments will simply not go to see a doctor (it may not be worth it if they expect to have to wait for a long time before being seen, for example), so that some possibly treatable disease goes untreated. But another important part of the

explanation lies in the substitution of the services of paramedical personnel (home visits by "health visitors," antenatal and postnatal care provided by nurses at "child welfare centres" and babies delivered by midwives) for physician services. Since paramedical personnel do not cost as much to train as doctors and are paid considerably less, this substitution certainly has contributed to keeping the cost of U.K. health services relatively low.

U.S. doctors have highest relative incomes

The differences in the unit cost of physician services between the three systems appear substantial. A recent OECD study gives the ratio of doctors' income to an average production worker's gross earnings (around 1974) as 5.6 in the U.S., 4.8 in Canada, and only 2.7 in the U.K.[53] In absolute dollar terms the C.M.A. lists the average net income of self-employed, fee-for-service physicians as \$41,200 for 1973;[54] for the U.S., the 1973 figure for physicians in private practice was estimated at about \$49,400.[55] For the U.K., the only figures I have been able to find refer to general practitioners, i.e., they exclude the specialists whose incomes tend to be higher. In 1974, the average payment by the NHS to a general practitioner was slightly less than \$25,000 when converted at the exchange rate of \$2.40/pound.[56] Even though the average income per physician (i.e., including specialists) would be higher, a comparison at the present time would also reflect the devaluation of the pound, so that the average income of British physicians can probably be estimated to be at most about half that of their North American colleagues. With higher rates of income tax in Britain, the after-tax differential of course would be even larger.

Is quality of care significantly different?

In the discussion of hospital services, I implicitly recognized that the number of patient-days might not be an unambiguous measure of the consumption of hospital services because the "quality" of a patient-day might differ between systems. One may raise a similar question in the case of physician services: are measures such as the number of doctors or the number of visits to a doctor good enough indicators of the quantity of services, or should one attempt to make adjustments for the "quality" of, say, an office visit? In the abstract, the answer to the latter question probably should be yes: one can imagine two countries in which the qualities of the average physician differed because of different amounts or quality of training, etc. But is this likely to be a relevant consideration in the context of a comparison of physician services between the U.S., U.K., and Canada?

Do the best doctors leave the U.K.?

In considering this question, one may first ask whether the income differences of physicians in itself cannot be taken as evidence of a quality difference. A basic principle in international trade analysis tells us that, after adjustment for transport costs or other impediments to international trade such as tariffs, the price of an internationally traded commodity of a given type should be about the same in all countries. While physician services in themselves are not exportable, doctors can move internationally. If the quality of physicians were the same in the three systems, would one not expect that physician net incomes in the three systems would be approximately the same? Conversely, could the net income differentials between the U.K. and the North American systems (which are reinforced by higher rates of U.K. income taxes) be taken as evidence that on the average, British doctors are less well trained and hence render a lower standard of service to their patients than do the North American doctors?

The answer to this question is not simple. First, one has to take account of cost-of-living differentials which may favour Britain, and also of the fact that many U.K. doctors may be prepared to sacrifice some income in favour of what many people perceive as the more relaxed life style in Europe. There are also substantial costs of moving and relocation. For these reasons, the existence of even substantial income differences need not be taken as necessarily inconsistent with the hypothesis that the quality of doctors is the same. Furthermore, there has in fact in the past existed a very substantial outmigration of physicians from the U.K. to North America, and there has been little evidence that the migration flow has been affected by considerations of the quality of the migrant doctors: immigrant physicians into the U.S. and Canada are required to write a qualifying examination before being allowed to practice, and large numbers of British doctors have had no difficulty passing this test and establishing themselves in practice. At the same time, this of course has meant a drain on the supply of physicians in the U.K., which has been partially compensated for by very substantial immigration of doctors to the U.K. from other countries, principally Commonwealth countries (over half of all NHS doctors are now immigrant doctors).

It is hard to say whether it is true, as appears to be widely believed, that this process has led to a situation where, on the average, doctors in the U.K. have received medical training of lower quality than in North America. There have not (at least until recently) been requirements for formal qualifying examinations for physicians immigrating to the U.K. from other Commonwealth countries. On the other hand, because of continuing links between medical schools in many Commonwealth countries and medical schools in Britain, one may assume that at least formally, there has been some tendency toward similarity of standards in the training of physicians throughout the Commonwealth. On balance, it seems reasonable to suspect that the level of formal qualification at the time of entry into practice in the U.K. has been somewhat lower than in North America (some doctors have also had language problems), and that many of the doctors who have left the U.K. have had better than average formal qualifications. Partly this would be expected because of age; younger doctors with more recent training would more likely be willing to try their hand at the North American qualifying examinations and to move than would older, established ones.

Even though the tentative conclusion of the above discussion is that the wide net income differential and the resulting migration flows have entailed a somewhat lower average level of formal qualification among U.K. doctors than would have applied if U.K. physician incomes had been as high as they are in North America, it does not of course follow that it would have been in the British interest to pay their physicians North American salaries. Formal training is not the only criterion for the quality of a doctor: length of time in practice, for example, may be as important. Given the uncertain link between the degree of formal training and the standard of patient care, it is by no means clear that the cost of preventing outmigration by substantial salary increases would have been justified. Indeed, as has been noted earlier, it has frequently been argued that too much money is being spent in the North American systems on providing physicians with a high level of formal training: many of the diagnostic and treatment functions performed by doctors, it is claimed, could be performed by paramedical personnel with shorter and less costly training, as in the U.K.

The rising spectre of malpractice suits

Before leaving the subject of the cost of physician services, mention should be made of the recently much-debated problem of malpractice suits and their cost in the U.S. There has been a trend in the past few years toward increasingly large settlements in such suits, and a related inflow of specialized lawyers into the field. As a result, there have been dramatic increases in the cost of malpractice insurance, especially for vulnerable specialties such as anaesthesiology, with the annual cost of insurance now sometimes running into tens of thousands of dollars. The cost of malpractice insurance, of course, will reflect itself in the fees for physician services, and while I do not have precise evidence, it is certainly plausible that this problem has made a substantial contribution to the rising cost of U.S. physician services. Part of the effect on total health care costs has been indirect: in addition to raising the cost of given services, the fear of malpractice suits has forced doctors to increasingly practice what is now known as "defensive medicine", i.e., to have patients undergo treatment or tests which are primarily motivated by the need to protect the doctor against such suits.

While there is little systematic evidence on which to base a comparison, one's casual impression certainly is that this is primarily a U.S. phenomenon, and while there might be a trend toward larger settlements and rising premiums for malpractice insurance in Canada and the U.K., the process has not gone nearly as far as in the U.S. Factors such as the prevalence in the U.S. of so-called contingency fees (where the lawyers' reimbursement is a proportion of the settlement) and the tendency toward a less personal doctor-patient relationship in a system increasingly dominated by specialist physicians rather than family doctors, have been suggested as explanations of this difference. In part, it may also be seen simply as a result of a gradual shift in public opinion, and in U.S. legal practice, toward a more stringent approach to the general problem of liability for damages, as evidenced by recent large settlements against car manufacturers in damage suits relating to injuries in auto accidents.

It has sometimes been argued that the patient's right to sue for malpractice, and rules that guarantee him an "adequate" settlement if he should win, constitute a necessary and desirable incentive on physicians to exercise care in diagnosis and choice of treatment.[56A] The extent to which the U.S. system and legal practice represents the appropriate degree of incentive in this respect is not clear; many observers claim that whatever reduction in risk to the patient which may have been accomplished has been small in relation to the direct and indirect costs, and that Canada would be ill served by following the U.S. example. This may or may not be true: in any event, it seems likely that the cost of malpractice insurance and the practice of "defensive medicine" have added substantially to the cost of health care in the U.S. and constitute part of the explanation for the higher cost of the American health care system in comparison with the U.K. and Canadian ones.

A comment on drug expenditures

Hospital costs and physician services are by far the largest components of the total cost of health services. The major item among the remaining expenditure categories (other than dental care) is the cost of drugs.[56B] As noted above, in the U.K., the cost of drugs is covered under the NHS, whereas in the U.S. and Canada, either most patients pay for them themselves or have to obtain private insurance. Not unexpectedly, the large expenditure on drugs in the U.K. has been regarded as a major problem: when the patient is covered under comprehensive insurance, neither he nor the doctor has any incentive to economize on their use, and with drugs being produced and sold by private firms, the field has been open for high-pressure marketing efforts by those firms, in large part aimed at the doctors. But drug expenditures are high in the North American systems as well, and casual observation suggests that it is at least as high as in the U.K.; a precise quantitative comparison is difficult both for conceptual reasons and because of lack of good data. In any event, it is unlikely that differences in the cost of drugs or various minor health services items will materially change the general picture of the quantity and cost of health services in the three systems, and I now turn to a summary of the evidence discussed so far, and to the conclusions to be drawn.

VII. CONCLUSIONS

The discussion in the preceding sections has been an attempt at a systematic comparison of three different approaches to resolving the problem of designing a health services system which represents a satisfactory compromise between the sometimes conflicting objectives of equitability, productive efficiency, and responsiveness to individual preferences. I compared the institutional organization of the systems, the available evidence on their performance in terms of prolonging life and maintaining good health generally, and on resource use and costs in the U.S., U.K., and Canadian systems. In the next few paragraphs, I will discuss what broad conclusions, if any, can be drawn from the evidence presented, and what the possible implications are for health services reform in Canada.

Data imperfections

Perhaps the first point that should be made concerns the quality of the data and hence the reliability of the statistical comparisons. The customary warnings that the data are not strictly comparable because of differing measurement procedures, heterogeneity of the quantities that are compared, and different definitions used across countries, apply with unusual force in the health services context. Further systematic studies of the quantitative aspects of the systems could certainly change the numbers, and could produce actual measurement of some aspects (such as the extent of untreated disease because of a shortage of facilities) which at this stage can only be discussed in a speculative way based on casual empiricism. *Nevertheless, I do not believe that the broad qualitative picture would be substantially changed even if better data were available.*

Saving money without risking lives

Turning first to what must be considered the primary measure of the success of a health services system, namely that of preventing deaths, it is remarkable that in spite of their differences, and in spite of the different environment and life styles in the three countries, the performances of the three health services systems appear to be so close together. This conclusion may be seen in one way as pessimistic: *it does not appear that even substantial increases in the amount of resources spent on health services, given current technology, will have much of an effect in terms of prolonging life.* In another way, it may be seen as somewhat reassuring: it suggests that *it may be possible to accomplish substantial savings in the amounts of resources used in the North American systems, at least, without "risking the lives" of the populations.* While this conclusion follows from the simple comparison of the mortality data between the U.K. and the North American systems, it is also consistent with those implicit in some of the recent North American debates on the subject: Marc Lalonde has strongly emphasized the limited contribution that the health care system can make to prolonging life expectancy relative to changes in life styles, as did some of the members of the health services panel on the Committee of Critical Choices for the U.S.[57]

The main difference between the systems which makes the similarity in life expectancy so remarkable, of course, is the very much lower amount of real resources being used in the U.K. health services system than in the North American ones. While there are obvious ambiguities in simple comparisons of per capita dollar amounts or percentages of GNP, the differences are much too large, and are supported by differences in measurements in physical units such as hospital beds or doctors per capita, to be dismissed as statistical aberrations.

How do the British do it?

How do the British do it? Some people would argue that they do it by substituting more efficient decision-making through a central public-sector administration for the wasteful workings of the market. Anyone who is familiar with the long history of inquiries into, and attempts at reform of, the administration of the NHS will find it difficult to accept this as the complete explanation. On the other hand, the analysis in the preceding chapters certainly supports the notion that the system of financial incentives facing doctors is of extreme importance in producing an efficient health services system, and it is significant that the British system is not based on fee-for-service but rather on salaried specialists and G.P.s partially remunerated on a capitation basis. This difference, rather than administrative centralization *per se,* may well be an important explanation for the lower costs in the U.K. system.

The British don't do it!
The alternative answer to the question how the British do it is that they do not, in fact, do it! While the British system allocates enough resources to produce about the same performance in terms of saving lives as in North America, it is argued that not enough resources are allocated to produce anywhere near the standard of treatment for "less serious" illness as prevails in North America. In the absence of good measures on the general level of health in the population, the evidence is mostly impressionistic, but it is nevertheless convincing: there are long waiting lists for "elective operations" in the U.K.; in many instances doctors simply will not recommend some types of potentially beneficial hospital treatment because they know that the facilities are not available, and the result is substantial amounts of untreated, or inadequately treated, disease. A small but growing literature now exists on appropriate methods for "rationing health care" when not enough is available.

This approach represents one way of saving the taxpayers' money while continuing to preserve "equity of access". But to my mind, it is not likely to be an approach that would be acceptable to Canadians: while everybody would presumably be in favour of paying lower taxes, I do not believe that most people would be happy with a system where local communities would have little voice in the closing of their neighbourhood hospital, where you would have to postpone minor surgery because of lack of hospital space, and where doctors dissatisfied with the system were emigrating en masse to the U.S.

Canada drifting in the British direction?
While this solution is unlikely to be what Canadians want, it

nevertheless seems to me that there are signs that we are drifting in this direction in spite of ourselves, as it were. We have now by and large resolved the issue of equitability of access to the health care system, as was done in the U.K. in 1948. We are, however, beginning to discover that a system with comprehensive, universal, tax-financed health insurance combined with a fee-for-service system of paying physicians, is likely to be a very expensive one. The lesson inherent in the success of the U.K. system in keeping costs down has not been lost on Canadian bureaucrats. On the one hand, there have been proposals to transfer physicians to a salary system (in Quebec, a decision to do so has been approved in principle). On the other hand, the current attempts by provincial governments to cut hospital costs (stimulated in part by the change in the form of federal support of health services) can be regarded as a first step on the road to more systematic rationing, and there is an increasing Canadian interest in the British literature on the principles of rationing.[58] Is this the route the Canadian system will take? Many people seem to think so, and to approve: Bennett and Krasny, in the series of *Financial Post* articles referred to above, for example, discuss the "need for rationing" of health care resources and outline ways in which it can be done.

Toward a market in health services

For those who, like myself, distrust the ability of the political process to formulate a system which combines efficiency in operating a complex industry such as health services through a centralized bureaucracy, with responsiveness to the wants of consumers and freedom from arbitrary political interference by special interest groups, this prospect is not appealing. The alternative, which will be discussed in some detail in Chapter Three, is a system which relies to a greater extent on the market mechanism. What lessons can be drawn from the experience of the U.S. in this regard?

Lessons from U.S. experience

In some respects, the lessons are not encouraging. While substantial progress has been made toward attaining the equitability-of-access objective (primarily through Medicare and Medicaid), a not insignificant part of the U.S. low-income population continues to have little or no health insurance protection, and undoubtedly there are some people who suffer ill health for which they are not being treated, for financial reasons. To my mind, this would not be acceptable to Canadians either: if the Canadian system were to put more reliance on the market mechanism in this area, a more satisfactory solution to the equitability problem would have to be found.

On the positive side, the U.S. health insurance industry has demonstrated the flexibility of the market mechanism: consumers can choose from a great variety of possible forms of insurance with different deductible and co-insurance provisions, or prepayment plans. Not all of this competition may have been beneficial: as noted above, some types of policies appear designed more to protect the interests of services providers than their beneficiaries, and it may be difficult for individual consumers to appreciate the importance of some of the exclusions and limitations. Competition has also made insurance virtually prohibitive for some high-risk groups. Hence, some types of selective regulation designed to protect the consumer is probably a desirable feature of a well-functioning health insurance market. Nevertheless, the basic advantage of the market mechanism in this area is there: the possibility for the individual to arrange his coverage in the way he wants it, given the cost and his personal circumstances.

Finally, the U.S. system in fact appears to have been somewhat more expensive than the Canadian one. On the face of it, this fact certainly appears to be inconsistent with the picture of an efficiently operating competitive system which was described in idealized form in Chapter One. There are a number of explanations that may be used to reconcile the two, however. First, the introduction of Medicare and Medicaid in the form of conventional insurance against fee-for-service clearly exerted an upward pressure on cost in the same way as the provincial plans in Canada. It also may have contributed to producing a slower rate of growth of prepayment plans or health maintenance organizations than would otherwise have taken place, and as was argued in Chapter One, effective competition from prepayment plans may be a necessary condition for a market system to perform efficiently when most of the population is insured. In addition, organized medicine in the U.S. has been remarkably successful in enforcing various kinds of policies that have reduced competition, as discussed above; this may be the most important explanation for the high costs of the system. Again, effective policies to deal with the influence of organized medicine would be an important aspect of a reform package in Canada which would lead to more reliance on the market. Finally, there has been the problem of the cost of malpractice insurance and "defensive medicine"; this issue would also have to be somehow resolved in a Canadian set of reforms of this sort.

In the last analysis, however, one can argue that a good part of the explanation for the high cost of the U.S. health care system is a simpler one. If the above factors have been quantitatively important, alternative public policies could have been pursued which would have slowed the rate of expenditure growth: Medicare and Medicaid could have been introduced in a different form, HMOs could have been encouraged more effectively, the influence of organized medicine resisted with more vigour. Since this was not done, one can argue that the U.S. system is in fact essentially what people in the U.S. want: consumers in a rich society are willing to pay for a large, high-quality, health services system. There is in fact some statistical evidence which may be taken to support this idea. If one correlates the percentage spent on health services in various countries with *per capita* GNP, one finds a positive correlation,[59] and one can also use the results to predict the proportion that an average country would spend on health services if it had the U.S. level of *per capita* GNP: the result is 6.7 per cent whereas for the U.K. it is 5.4 per cent. Thus, in general, international experience would lead one to *expect* that a country like the U.S. would devote a relatively large fraction of its GNP on health services. But the fact that people in such societies seem to be willing to pay for a large health services system, regardless of its institutional form, is not an argument *against* a market-oriented system: if that is what consumers want, an efficiently operating market will give it to them. On the other hand, if the system has functioned imperfectly and consumers have been made to pay more than they "really" want, a more efficient market mechanism will produce a smaller and cheaper health services system. Hence, if the issue of equity can be resolved, and if there are ways of making the competitive forces work reasonably well, we will get more or less the system that individuals want, i.e., an efficient one in the economist's sense. In the final chapter, I turn to the issue of policies through which these problems could be approached in a hypothetical health services reform in Canada.

APPENDIX: THE CASE OF SWEDEN

At the beginning of this chapter, I noted that a possible alternative to the choice of the U.K. as an example of an essentially centralized health services system, would have been Sweden. The purpose of this Appendix is to provide some very basic information on the organization and performance of the Swedish health care system, and to speculate a little on the difference it would have made to the conclusions just drawn if Sweden had been chosen instead.

Universal, compulsory, comprehensive insurance
As in the U.K., equality of access to health care in Sweden has been accomplished by compulsory, universal, comprehensive, tax-financed health insurance. Most health care costs are financed out of local taxation at the county level (about 3/4 of the total), with the public health insurance agency and the central government paying most of the rest; fees collected from the patient amount to only about 1 per cent of the total.[60]

Deterrent fees paid by patient
Contrary to the U.K. system, there are some "deterrent fees", but they are small; in 1975, they were 12 crowns (about $3) per visit to a public GP, and 50 per cent of outpatient medication up to a maximum of 15 crowns (a little less than $4) were to be paid by the patient. Hospital care, however, is entirely tax-financed with no direct cost to the user. Persons seeking treatment with a private GP (who continue to practice, but mostly in the large cities) are reimbursed 75 per cent of the cost according to an established scale. It should also be noted that the total cost to the patient of ill health is further reduced in Sweden by a relatively liberal legislation regarding paid sick leave. In recent political debate, it has been argued that these provisions have contributed to the high rates of absenteeism among Swedish employees, and it is likely

that they have also led to an increased rate of utilization of health services for minor illness, though I am not aware of any systematic studies demonstrating this.

Doctors are salaried employees
Most physicians in Sweden are salaried employees, though (as in the U.K.), some doctors continue to practice privately on a fee-for-service basis, either part-time or full-time. The extent to which private practice is to be allowed, however, is the subject of considerable debate, and the trend has been toward more complete reliance on a salary system. Unlike the U.K., the capitation principle has not been used, and the emphasis on primary care by GPs has not been as great as in the U.K.

High quality
Turning to the evidence on the performance of the Swedish health care system, one's overall impression is that it is of exceptionally high quality. By most measures, mortality in Sweden is one of the lowest in the world; in 1971 it had the highest life expectancy at age one of any country, both for males and females.[61] It can be argued that environmental and life style factors account for a good part of this performance: the environment is still comparatively clean in Sweden, high taxes on liquor and tobacco and a variety of anti-smoking campaigns have moderated Swedish drinking and smoking habits, and we have all seen the slim and fit-looking 65-year-old Swede bouncing along effortlessly beside the overweight and sweating 30-year-old Canadian in the television advertisement. But even so, the mortality evidence is certainly consistent with a high-quality health care system, and for both pre-natal and infant mortality which are widely regarded as good measures of the effectiveness of care, Sweden again ranks first in the world.[62] Furthermore, there is little of the evidence of untreated "minor" disease which I discussed at length for the case of the U.K. There are some complaints about the impersonality of a system which relies primarily on salaried hospital physicians and de-emphasizes the traditional relationship between the patient and his GP-family doctor, and even instances where bureaucratic foul-ups have had relatively serious medical consequences for individual patients.

On the whole, however, the picture is one of a high-quality health services system which delivers good care to everybody.

High cost

The other side of the coin is the cost. According to a recent OECD study,[63] Sweden and the U.S. are the two countries in the world which devoted the largest proportion of their GDP to health services in 1974: 7.3 per cent and 7.4 per cent. The corresponding figure for Canada in that year is listed as 6.8 per cent, and for the U.K., 5.2 per cent. It is interesting to note that relative to the U.S. and Canada, a smaller proportion of this goes to physician services. Sweden has fewer physicians per head than either of these countries, and many fewer consultations per capita.[64] The very high cost of Swedish health care appears to be primarily a phenomenon of large expenditures on hospitals. One source lists Sweden as having 694 beds per hundred thousand people in 1971. The corresponding figure for the Canadian system was 574, and the U.S. even lower.[65]

How does one explain this pattern? In part, it undoubtedly reflects demographic and environmental factors: Sweden has a very large proportion of older people, and has a low population density which may necessitate a network of many relatively small hospitals. But it is also likely that the high cost reflects the consequences of particular features of the organization of the Swedish system. The decentralization of taxing and spending powers to the county level has made it easier for local politicians to build monuments to themselves in the form of well-appointed hospitals. The relative lack of emphasis on primary care through GPs is likely to have led to a higher rate of hospital utilization, and the low level of deterrent fees, as well as the sick-leave provisions referred to above, must have raised the utilization rates at the patients' initiative over and above what it otherwise would have been.

How do the Swedes do it?

On the basis of this very brief description of the Swedish system, what can be said about the relevance of the Swedish experience to the issue of a Canadian health services reform? First of all, an obvious conclusion to be drawn from a comparison of the U.K. and Swedish cases, is that transferring health services provision to the public sector does not by itself solve the problem of providing high-quality care at low cost. A good part of the answer to the question, "how do the Swedes do it?" appears to be that they spend a lot of money on it. One of my conclusions at the end of Chapter Two was that the U.K. version of a centralized system did not provide a good model for the Canadian system, because we would not be willing to accept that degree of reduction in the quality of care. The conclusion to be drawn here, I believe, is that the Swedish example does not provide a good model either, because in Canada we would not be prepared to accept the cost. Presumably, what Canadians want is a system somewhere in between, and again, it seems to me that giving the market more of a chance to operate would give us an opportunity to find out implicitly what sort of a system that is, without the political soul-searching, administrative complexities, and wrangling with organized medicine that would arise if the question were to be answered through the political process within the framework of a further centralization of the health services sector.

NOTES

[1]Most of the information regarding the history and present organization of the NHS comes from [6].

[2]See [13], pp. 82-88.

[3]Quote is from [6], p. 12.

[4]Figures are based on the 1974 edition of [6] which contains an Appendix on Private Medicine.

[5][7], p. 9.

[6]Quotes are from the 1974 edition of [6], Appendix 1. The 1977 edition has deleted these quotes.

[7]The main source for the information in this paragraph is [27].

[8]Unless otherwise indicated, the factual information in this section comes from [19], which is an excellent comprehensive study of U.S. health insurance.

[9]Recent statistics in [42], Table III, p. 75 indicate that between 1970 and 1974, the trend toward more comprehensive types of insurance continued. Growth was especially rapid in insurance against the cost of physician office and home visits, out-of-hospital prescribed drugs, private-duty nursing, and so on.

[9A]See [19], p. 29.

[10]See [23].

[11][22].

[11A]See [26A], pp. 73-74 and reference there.

[11B]See 26A, p. 65 and reference there.

[12][24], Table 13, p. 69, shows increases in the number of physicians per hundred thousand people between 1960-70 of 32.7 per cent for Canada and 17.9 per cent for the U.S.

[13][19], p. 44. See also [24A], Ch. 3, for an excellent general analysis of hospital efficiency.

[14]See, e.g., [25], especially p. 70.

[15][1], p. 6.

[16][21], This essay provides a good description of the evolution of public health insurance in Canada.

[17][21], p. 14.

[18][21], p. 14.

[19][30], pp. 132-134.

[20][10], p. 440; [30], pp. 131-132.

[21][30], p. 128.

[22][21], pp. 57-58.

[23][1], p. 9.

[24][10], p. 441.

[25]Sources were [5], Tables C-2, and B-4, and [34].

[26]Sources were [35], Table 2 for the surgery rates; other variables as in the previous note.

[27]Most of the information on HSOs in Canada was obtained in a personal interview with Mr. Joseph T. Altopiedi of the Ontario Ministry of Health.

[28][15]. For a critical discussion of this report, see [24A], Ch. 4.

[29][8], pp. 20-22.

[30]Sources: for the U.S. [42], Table 85, p. 60. For the U.K. [39] and [40], Table 34, p. 51 (1975 and 1976 issues); for Canada [46], Tables 2, 3; pp. 58-59. U.S. figures in the first two columns are for 1950 and 1960 respectively.

[31]See [24], Table 6, p. 62. Figures refer to 1971.

[32]Sources: for Canada [37], Table 9, pp. 24-26; for the U.S. [42], Table 85, p. 60 (first two columns are 1949-51 and 1959-61 averages, respectively); for the U.K., [40], Table 32, p. 48.

[33]Sources: for U.S. compiled by author from [42], Table 90, p. 63. For the U.K., compiled from [39], Table 31, p. 47; for Canada, from [37], Table 10, p. 28.

[34]Sources: compiled by author from [37], Table 15, pp. 44-63, [39], Table 31, p. 47, and [42], Table 93, p. 65.

[35][20].

[36]See, e.g., [45], pp. 26-27 and references there; also [2].

[37]Sources: compiled from [39], Table 66, p. 83 and Table 31, p. 47 for the U.K.; for Canada, from [31] and [36].

[38]From [40], Table 61, p. 77.

[39]Sources: [42], Table 130, p. 84 and 68, p. 51; [31], Table A, p. 14, [37], Table 9, p. 22; [40], Table 31, p. 47 and Table 61, p. 77. For the U.K. and Canada "separations" were used rather than admissions.

[40]See Chapter 1, Notes 1 and 5 for sources.

[41]For U.S. and Canada, figures refer to general and allied special hospitals (i.e., excluding psychiatric). Sources: for U.S., [42], Table 130, p. 84; Canada, [32], Table 1A, p. 18 and Table 1, p. 17; U.K., [40], Table 61, p. 77. Hospitalization episodes for the U.K. include psychiatric cases, and the number of beds in non-psychiatric departments was estimated by assuming that occupancy rates were the same in psychiatric and non-psychiatric departments.

[42]Computed from [31], Table A, p. 14.

[43][41], Table 1, p. 75, and Table 25, p. 90.

[44]Sources: Canada, [32], Table 12, p. 34; U.S. [42], Table 128, p. 82. The U.S. figure refers to non-federal hospitals only.

[45]Computed from [39], Table 61, p. 77, Table 44, p. 50, and Table 6, p. 7. Fiscal year figures were interpolated to get calendar year figures, and the ratio of patient day cost in a psychiatric to a non-psychiatric department was set at .42.

[46]Source: [16], pp. 84-7, 374-81.

[47][1], p. 12.

[48]Compiled from [43], p. 39.

[49][1], p. 12 and [43], p. 39.

[50]Sources: [40], Table 64, pp. 80-81, [43], p. 52, and [5], Table B3. The Canadian figure includes interns and residents.

[51][24], Table 13, p. 69, lists 127, 154 and 151 for England and Wales, the U.S. and Canada respectively, in 1971.

[52][28], pp. 131, 135 and 101.

[53][28], Table 9, p. 24.

[54][5], Table C2.

[55][43], p. 59.

[56]Compiled from [39], Table 61, p. 77.

[56A]See [29B].

[56B]For an excellent discussion of "the economics of drugs," see [24A], Ch. 8.

[57]See essay by A. Wildawsky, pp. 105-123, in [18].

[58]See, e.g., [8].

[59]Data sources: [28], Table 4, p. 10, and [46].

[60][38], p. 14. Most of the institutional information in this section comes from this source.

[61][24], Table 6, p. 62.

[62][24], Table 4, p. 60.

[63][28], Table 4, p. 10.

[64][24], Table 13, p. 69 lists the number of physicians per 100,000 in the U.S., Canada, and Sweden as 154, 151 and 139, respectively. [7], pp. 135, 101, and 127 list the number of physician consultations as 5.0 (1974), 4.6 (1973) and 2.0 (1974) respectively.

[65][24], Table 15, p. 71.

Chapter 3
TOWARDS A SOLUTION

I. INTRODUCTION

In Chapter One, I outlined in some detail the way in which one could envisage an efficiently operating market-oriented health services system. I also considered the major objections that have been raised by opponents of such a system, and I concluded that one of the reasons why one might expect to observe a trend away from reliance on the market in this area was the perceived difficulties in combining a market-oriented health care system with an equitable distribution of health services.

The equity-efficiency quandary

As I argued at the end of Chapter Two, the empirical evidence from the U.K., the U.S., and Canada can be interpreted to be broadly consistent with the idea that there is an equity/efficiency conflict of this kind. While the U.K. system in one sense can be said to have resolved the question of equitable access, there are indications that the system is not particularly efficient in the economist's sense. In Canada, the equity problem has also been pretty much resolved but costs are growing at an alarming rate and the reaction has been to move toward policy measures which have substantially reduced, if not totally eliminated, the role of the market mechanism, and which are bringing us gradually closer to the U.K.-type system. In the U.S., the market system essentially determined resource allocation in the health services field before the advent of Medicare and Medicaid; at that time, the evidence seemed to be that there were substantial differences in the access of different population groups to "adequate" care, however defined. With Medicare and Medicaid the equity objective has again been attained to a substantial extent; but the evidence also points strongly to the emergence of the same, or in fact even more severe, problems of expenditure growth in the U.S. than have been experienced in Canada.

The objective of this chapter, therefore, is to explore

possible compromise solutions to the efficiency/equity quandary, and, in particular, to try to show that it is possible to exploit some of the advantages of a market-oriented health services system while at the same time preserving the principle that low-income people should be protected against the worst economic consequences of ill health. The chapter is organized as follows. In Section II, I consider alternative ways of resolving the problem of equity in the provision of health services. Section III contains a discussion of ways of restoring competition between providers of health services, without creating a situation in which patients are short-changed by low-quality treatment, and without sacrificing the equity principle. In Section IV, I summarize what I would consider an "ideal" compromise solution, and I then go on to discuss the problem of political feasibility, and the question whether there are partial policy measures which, while not attaining the "ideal", would at least take us part of the way there.

II. EQUITY IN HEALTH SERVICES

A. ALTERNATIVE DEFINITIONS

When considering the problem of alternative means of ensuring equity in the provision of health services, we must first inquire as to what exactly is meant by "equity" in this context.

Is the U.K. system equitable, for example?
As I argued in Chapter One, the simplest notion is that everybody should have access to the best possible medical facilities regardless of cost, which in practice would have to mean free of charge to the user. But as I also argued there, this definition doesn't make sense, at least not if interpreted literally. To take an example from another market, it clearly would be absurd to define an equitable housing policy by the idea that everybody should be able to enjoy housing of the best available kind regardless of cost. Similarly, once one recognizes that there *is* considerable room for choice in the health services area, it becomes clear that the "best available" medical services would be expensive indeed: all hospital accommodation would be in private wards, nobody should have to wait for a doctor's

appointment, and there would be no limits on the number of diagnostic tests that a patient or his doctor could require for a particular problem, or for hospital treatment even for non-serious ailments. As was amply illustrated in Chapter Two, in the U.K. system which is generally regarded as quite "equitable", none of these conditions even remotely apply.

Universal access to the best available care is impossible!

Recognition that "universal access to the best available care" is an impossible definition of "equity", is of fundamental importance if there is to be rational discussion of the equity/ efficiency quandary. If this is not recognized, we will be forever furtively struggling with the problem of trying to ensure that everybody gets exactly the same kind of health care when they are ill. This struggle is a losing one either way. If the "best available care" concept is taken seriously, it would undoubtedly be too expensive—more expensive than society can afford or would be willing to pay for. If costs are to be contained, the standard level of care will not be "the best available", and society is then faced with the problems of rationing of health services. What, for example, is to be done about those people who are willing to pay on their own for more health services than society will provide? Either one lets them do so, and uneasily accepts the resulting "two-class" system, or one employs legislative action to prevent them from doing so. This is a problem that the U.K. has been wrestling with for years, and there is continuous debate over the question whether it is "proper" that NHS hospitals should make beds available to patients who are paying for their own health services outside the NHS system and are treated by their own doctors.

Equity must be defined pragmatically

Once these difficulties have been recognized, it becomes clear that "equity" in the provision of health services has to be defined in a more pragmatic way, and the definition will essentially amount to a value judgment. What is it we are trying to accomplish by achieving "equity"? The sensible answer, it seems to me, is that we are trying to do roughly the same thing as the progressive income tax and the welfare system are supposed to do, namely to ensure that no individual in society falls below a "decent" standard of living through bad luck. Thus, the equity problem in health care is simply the problem of ensuring that no individual who has the bad luck of getting sick should be denied a "decent" standard of care for financial reasons. What is a "decent" standard of health care is obviously a value judgment, just as is the definition of a "decent" standard of living for welfare recipients. And the battle cry, "Universal access to a minimum level of adequate care!" is perhaps not as stirring as "The best available care for all!" But it is the only sensible one.

Health care only one of the problems

Before leaving the question of defining equity in health services, it is worth observing that there also exists another more restrictive viewpoint concerning "equity" in this context, namely that there is no reason why society should concern itself with the consumption of health care services in particular; I touched on this in Chapter One. The problem with low-income families is that they have low incomes in general; they are therefore able to consume only relatively small amounts of *all* goods and services, not just health care. Society's responsibility toward low-income families thus is to provide them with higher incomes in general, and let each individual family decide for itself how much health care services to consume, or rather how much health insurance to buy. If the political mechanism can produce agreement of some sort on what constitutes a minimally acceptable level of income, and hence of consumption of goods and services in general when people decide for themselves what to consume, why should we not accept the health services consumption that people themselves decide on, as "minimally adequate" as well?

To my mind, this argument has very considerable merit for poor people who do not become *seriously* ill, i.e., those who in any given year consume nothing more than "routine" health services dealing with relatively minor problems. Society does not concern itself with the question whether a welfare recipient chooses to spend his cheque on fixing his car or buying a bicycle; why should it concern itself with the question whether he buys a bicycle or spends it on elective surgery for a minor health problem? I will return to this viewpoint at a later stage when I argue in favour of allowing anybody to have a deductible clause in his health insurance contract.

How to deal with catastrophic illness

As I briefly noted in Chapter One, however, there are two main objections to be raised against this view in the context of "catastrophic" illness. First, one can argue that the choice of health insurance is such an extreme case of decision-making under uncertainty that there is a case for society to intervene and ensure more protection, especially for low-income families, than people would voluntarily choose to provide for themselves. Second, one can consider health insurance as a device through which individuals arrange to transfer income from themselves when they are well, to themselves when they have the bad luck to become seriously ill, just as a progressive income tax represents a way through which society arranges to transfer resources from individuals who earn adequate incomes to those who, through various forms of bad luck, do not have the capacity to do so. When the question is seen in this light, it becomes clear that there is no reason why the amount of insurance protection that poor people would choose to acquire against the consequences of ill health should be the same as that which society at large would like to provide for poor and sick people. Whereas a progressive tax (and welfare) system to some extent compensates for lost income during illness, the problem with being sick is not just that of lost income, but much more importantly, that of the possibility of heavy expenditure on medical services.

If one sympathizes with either or both of these views, as indeed most people seem to be doing implicitly, there *is* a case for public interference with individual decisions regarding health insurance protection. But the important point to note here is that it only establishes a case for *compulsory health insurance corresponding to some minimally adequate level*. It clearly does not imply anything about uniform coverage for everybody, or about comprehensive coverage. Nor does it establish a case for tax-financed health insurance; and perhaps most importantly, it has no implication whatsoever for the question whether health services (or health insurance) should be provided publicly or privately through a market-oriented system.

B. EQUITY IN A MARKET-ORIENTED SYSTEM

To clarify those ideas, consider as an example the present Ontario system, and suppose one agrees that at the present time it provides at least an adequate standard of insurance protection for everybody covered by OHIP. The health services provided by the system are financed by a combination of OHIP premiums and tax revenue.

Suppose now that the governments (provincial and federal) were to decide to stop all subsidization of health services. This would, in the first instance, mean that all public expenditure on health services would have to be financed out of public-sector insurance revenue which in turn would mean that premiums would have to be substantially increased. This of course would be especially burdensome on low-income families. But the point is that if subsidies to the health services sector were eliminated, there would be excess government revenue which could be used for tax reductions. In particular, it would theoretically be possible to distribute this excess revenue in such a way that no family or individual would be worse off with the higher OHIP premium than they had been prior to the premium increase.

In itself, this observation is trivial: all it says is that *somebody* is paying the full cost of the present consumption of health services, and that in principle, we could redistribute income, through the tax system, in such a way that no family would be worse off even if it had to pay an actuarially fair insurance premium. But it does illustrate the point that a system in which everybody pays an actuarially fair premium for a prescribed minimum level of health insurance need not be an inequitable one, if the tax system is adjusted accordingly. I will return below to the practical problem of precisely *how* the tax system would have to be adjusted to accomplish this.

As long as health insurance is provided through a single public insurance agency, therefore, it really is pretty much a matter of indifference whether compulsory health insurance is financed through taxes or insurance premiums, or some combination thereof, provided the tax burden can be redistributed in such a way that premium-financed insurance does not become too much of a burden on low-income families. But suppose that one wants to allow for the possibility of insurance provision by private insurance agencies as well. In that case, the distinction becomes crucial: unless the premium a person saves by switching from a public insurance scheme reflects the full actuarial cost of that insurance, private agencies will not be competing on equal terms.

Define a minimum standard of insurance and leave it at that?

This line of argument also establishes the fact that, as long as equity in the provision of health services is defined as a minimally adequate coverage for everybody, it should be possible essentially to achieve the equity objective in a system where health insurance is provided by private insurance agencies alone, or by both private and public agencies. The equity objective could be attained by precisely defining the minimally adequate package of health insurance by which all persons would have to be covered; the question whether this coverage would be provided by a public or a private agency may be important from a practical point of view, but public insurance would not be required as a matter of principle. It should be emphasized again that a shift to compulsory premium-financed health insurance, even if it were privately provided, need not worsen the distribution of income, provided that income tax schedules were readjusted to allow for the effect of higher premiums.

Universal coverage does not imply public provision

It should also be clear that the provision of minimally adequate insurance protection for everybody does not necessarily imply that health services would have to be provided exclusively by the public sector. As I argued in the previous chapters, the pressure for increasing public sector involvement results from the costly nature of a system where everybody is covered by universal comprehensive insurance of the conventional kind, and where providers are paid on a fee-for-service basis. I also argued that in a system in which there was competition between fee-for-service and alternative forms of provision (such as prepaid group practice or HMO-type organizations), costs would have less of a tendency to rise and there would be less reason for public sector involvement. But the objective of providing universal minimally adequate coverage would certainly not be inconsistent with the existence of privately operated HMOs, say. On the contrary, as long as consumers could choose between public or private insurance, and as long as public insurance were not subsidized out of tax revenue, one would expect private HMOs to be able to compete effectively against public insurance, as well as against conventional private insurance under a fee-for-service system, in providing the specified minimum package.

III. A COMPETITIVE HEALTH SERVICES INDUSTRY FOR CANADA

In this section, I turn to the question of ways in which public policy measures can be used to restore and strengthen competition and efficiency in the various sectors of a market-oriented health services industry. I assume throughout that equity has been achieved by some scheme of the sort described in the preceding section, i.e., there is a minimum prescribed package of health insurance that everybody must have, but there is no direct subsidy for health insurance or health services: the impact of the cost of compulsory health insurance on low-income families is assumed to have been compensated by modifications of the income tax schedule or the welfare system. I begin by considering the question of competition in the health insurance industry, and further discuss ways in which the establishing of prepayment plans such as HMOs could be encouraged. I then go on to the issues of competition and efficiency in the provision of health services, including hospital and physician services.

A. HEALTH INSURANCE: THE ROLE OF LEGISLATION

In any health services system where there is a substantial role for the public sector in providing insurance or health services, the importance of the private health insurance industry is essentially determined by the form that the public sector intervention takes. Thus, in the present Canadian systems, private health insurance is of very minor importance because provincial plans cover more or less the entire population, coverage is highly comprehensive, and hospital services are for all practical purposes publicly provided with a substantial part of hospital revenue coming directly from taxes rather than as direct payment for services rendered.

Creating conditions for competition

If the system were to move in the direction of "minimally adequate" compulsory insurance financed entirely out of premiums, there would obviously be more room for private insurance to compete even if public sector insurance schemes were to continue to exist and to offer the prescribed minimum insurance package at cost. First, private insurance could continue to offer insurance supplementary to the minimum package for those who wanted it; second, there would be no reason why private insurance could not also compete with the public schemes in offering the basic compulsory package if it could be provided at lower cost in the private sector.

The importance of supplementary insurance provided by the private sector would clearly depend to a large extent on the precise content of the compulsory package. An important question which must now be faced, therefore, is precisely what one would like to see contained in such a package.

As was discussed at some length in Chapter Two, health insurance firms in the U.S. market have designed a wide range of insurance contracts with various exclusions and limitations which are intended to reduce the expected cost of indemnity payments and hence make it possible to offer the contracts at lower premium cost. On the "high" side, there are limitations on the total amounts of liability per disease episode, or on total payments during some specified time period. There may also be exclusions relating to the cost of specific types of particularly expensive treatment for specific conditions (such as renal dialysis, or long-term psychiatric care). On the "low" side, there may be deductibles of various magnitude, and there may be co-insurance provisions of one form or another. If one were to designate a "minimum adequate" insurance package as compulsory, are there restrictions of this kind that should be incorporated?

No limit to liability?

To answer that question, one first has to be precise about what it is that the system is supposed to accomplish. The purpose of making basic insurance compulsory was discussed above: it could be defined as that of ensuring protection for everybody, and particularly low-income families, against the possibility of financial disaster as a consequence of the cost of treatment of *major,* unpredictable illness. When seen in this light, it becomes pretty clear that if it were to achieve its purpose, a compulsory health insurance package should not have any upper limits either by disease episode or by any particular time period. Using the terminology of the current debate on national health insurance in the U.S., it would have to provide full protection against "financial catastrophe" of any magnitude resulting from the cost of necessary treatment of major illness. Private insurance companies may balk at the idea of an absolutely open-ended commitment, and there probably would be no harm in allowing some arbitrary but very high number, such as $1 million as a *minimum* upper limit. Cases where the cost of treatment for an illness exceeds that number must be extremely rare, and the total cost to the government of taking residual responsibility for costs in excess of this limit would obviously be very small.

Problems of advanced medical technology and experimental cures

While this principle seems to me an indispensable part of any system purporting to resolve the equity issue, some qualifications may be necessary at the practical level. The first one has to do with changing medical technology and the continued development of new but frequently expensive ways of treating serious illness. Examples which come to mind are the various experimental courses of treatment for different types of cancer, the continuing development of organ transplant techniques, experimentation with sophisticated types of artificial limbs and artificial vision, and there are doubtless many others. Should compulsory health insurance provide payment for any such course of treatment for anybody whose doctor asks for it? It appears to me that the answer to this must be no. The very nature of "experimental" courses of treatment implies that they will at first be available only to a selected few patients, in *any* health care system; the selection is made in such a way as to add as much as possible to medical knowledge, not on the basis of the "need" of the patient. Since they cannot, therefore, be available to everybody, there is no reason why everybody should carry insurance against their cost. The proper way of paying for the cost of experimental procedures which can be considered part of medical research, rather than as the application of medical technology for the benefit of the individual, is to have them included as part of medical research in general, and to meet their cost out of research budgets at no cost to the patients selected. Since medical research potentially benefits all of society, it should also be paid for by all of society, i.e., out of general tax revenue. In the economist's jargon, "knowledge" is a public good. The application of existing knowledge for the benefit of an individual patient, by contrast, benefits only the patient, and should also be paid for by the beneficiary himself, through his insurance.

The upshot of this discussion, therefore, is that while there should in principle be no upper limit on the amount of a person's insurance against the cost of treatment which is considered "accepted practice," the exclusion of "experimental courses of treatment" means that these categories would have to be well defined in the standard insurance package, i.e., it might be necessary to specifically exclude certain types of treatment, as indeed is done in many private health insurance contracts in the U.S. industry.

Artificial prolongation of life

A second qualification which seems to me a potentially important one concerns the recently much discussed issue of the "artificial" prolongation of the life of accident victims or terminally ill patients. Legislation has been proposed in the U.S. and Canada which would make it possible for an individual to write a clause in his will to the effect that he specifically requests no prolongation of his life by "extraordinary or artificial means" in case of terminal illness, and there have been well-publicized cases where families have gone to court in order for life-sustaining treatment of their dying relatives to be stopped. But if many, perhaps most, individuals would not want this type of treatment, should one force them to pay for insurance which would cover it? It seems reasonable again to answer this question in the negative. But it should be noted that to do so would mean to say also that those who would want to have their life prolonged by any means, even in cases of irreversible brain damage, say, would have to pay extra for insurance which would guarantee such treatment, and this might be a morally repugnant argument to those who consider it society's responsibility to preserve human life in whatever form. Ultimately, the answer requires a value judgment.

Chronic and old age care

A third qualification to the principle of no upper limit and comprehensive coverage of all types of health care costs concerns long-term chronic care for the aged, or in particular, whether insurance against old-age home or nursing home care should be covered by compulsory insurance. With predictions for an increasing proportion of older people in Canada over the next few decades, and a consequent rapid expansion in the demand for these types of care, this question may be one of the more important ones to be faced by Canadian health policy planners over the next few years.

To my mind, there are good reasons why long-term care in old-age homes or nursing homes should not be covered. Many of the functions performed in such institutions can also be performed in the old person's home, by relatives or by visiting nurses, etc. Those forms of care may be less costly; more importantly, many old people would probably *prefer* to be cared for at home rather than in institutions whenever this is possible. But if this is so, there seems to be no good reason why one should force such people and their families to pay for insurance against the cost of institutional care which they would not want to use. It is worth noting in this context that the question whether insurance against the cost of institutional care should be made compulsory is quite different from the problem of ensuring that old people have a decent income. The solution to the latter problem may well require compulsory participation in some form of a social security system (as in the U.S.) or a public sector pension scheme (as in Canada). Once it has been guaranteed that every old person will have a reasonable income, however, there seems to be no reason why old people should not be given the choice whether to spend it on institutional care or in other ways, as they see fit. Forcing everybody to carry insurance covering the cost of institutional care obviously constitutes a strong financial incentive for both the old people and their families to choose *it* rather than home care even when they would otherwise prefer the latter.

All of the above are practical qualifications, however, and the fundamental principle remains essentially the same: if a standard package of health insurance is to be made compulsory in order to resolve the equity problem, it should provide comprehensive coverage against the cost of *necessary* treatment of major illness with no exclusions or upper limits on the amounts payable.

What about deductibles?

In the terminology used earlier, this principle refers to limitations on the "high" side. As was noted before, in the private health insurance industry it is also common to offer contracts with various limitations on the "low" side, i.e., deductibles and co-insurance provisions. Would such limitations be compatible with the equity objective in a system based on a compulsory insurance package?

The answer is not obvious. To those who feel that an individual's decision whether to seek medical treatment of any kind, or a doctor's choice between alternative courses of treatment, should be completely independent of financial circumstances, "equity" would presumably require that there be no limitations of any kind. But this definition of "equity" is equivalent to accepting the principle of "the best possible medical care for everybody, regardless of cost" which I rejected before as an unworkable criterion for a health services system. What sets health services apart from other goods and services is the fact that illness is *sometimes* so serious that the individual has little choice: he *has* to have specific treatment even if it is very expensive; and also the fact that he may be badly informed about the probabilities and costs of treatment of some serious diseases. But as I discussed earlier, a very large proportion of health services are not used in the treatment of serious disease but rather to deal in a more or less routine fashion with more or less routine ailments, for which there may be a considerable latitude for discretionary choice by the patient or his doctor with respect to what services to use. There seems to be no good reason why an equitable system should *require* that everybody should be insured against the cost of such minor misfortunes. If equity requires that

161

everybody should be insured against the cost of treating a sore throat or having an appendectomy, why doesn't it also require insurance against the cost of repairing a broken down plumbing system or car?

Deductibles don't impair equity

On those grounds, it therefore seems reasonable to permit some limitations in the form of deductibles and co-insurance provisions in a compulsory health insurance package, without considering this as a sacrifice of the equity objective. The potential advantages of deductibles or co-insurance have already been extensively discussed in Chapter One: by making the individual responsible for paying the cost of the health services he consumes, it provides a direct financial incentive not to overuse the system and to look for low-cost, efficient health care. If it is true that an excessive use of health services for relatively minor ailments and a lack of price competition among services providers are major causes of the rapid growth in health care expenditure, a substantial deductible may be a necessary condition to reduce that growth if health insurance is to be compulsory and fee-for-service provision is to continue in existence. Co-insurance provisions have similar effects as deductibles, and may be desirable as a means for maintaining an incentive for patients and doctors to seek low-cost care even for relatively more serious conditions and hence costlier treatment.

A summary of characteristics of an adequate insurance plan

The discussion in the preceding paragraphs can now be summarized as follows. If the equity objective in the health services sector is to be met by a system of a "minimally adequate" package of compulsory health insurance, it has been argued that this package would have to be a comprehensive one, covering the treatment of essentially all types of major illness with no exceptions or upper limits on the total amount payable. In order to provide those individuals who are so inclined with a reward for seeking low-cost, efficient treatment in cases where there exists some real choice a substantial deductible (or some combination of deductible and co-insurance provisions) should be permitted. For similar reasons, individuals would not be *required* to carry insurance against the cost of old-age home or nursing home care, although of course anybody who would want to carry such insurance would be permitted to do so.

B. THE MARKET FOR HEALTH INSURANCE

Suppose now that present health insurance arrangements in Canada were to be replaced by legislation requiring everybody to hold a compulsory health insurance package along the lines just discussed. The issue then arises what changes one would expect to see in the market for health insurance.

A continuing role for government plans?
To consider this issue, one first would have to decide whether the present provincial insurance plans would continue to operate, albeit in modified form. It seems to me that political realities clearly are such that they would. Public sector involvement in the health insurance industry is widely and sometimes fervently supported, and the only sensible question to ask must concern the role they are to play in the system, not whether they are to exist. In addition, as I will discuss below, they may well have important functions in terms of providing competitive pressure on the private health insurance industry, even in a market-oriented system.

The most important function, then, which would be assumed by existing provincial plans would be that of administering an insurance plan corresponding to the compulsory coverage required by legislation. Apart from the method of financing and premium setting, to which I will return below, and from the fact that the plans would now contain a major deductible, their role would initially be quite similar to the one they have in the system as it now exists.

The role for private insurance
The private health insurance industry in Canada at the present time obviously plays a somewhat limited role: it is confined to issuing policies which supplement and extend the coverage provided by the provincial plans. Examples include plans which insure against the cost of drugs, prescription eyeglasses, private-duty nursing, hospital accommodation at the semi-

private level, and similar minor items relative to the health services industry as a whole.

In the alternative system, as long as most people continued to buy their basic compulsory package from public-sector agencies, the main function of private agencies would continue to be that of supplementing the public plan. Because the latter would contain a deductible, private firms might be able to generate some additional business by offering policies to cover the deductible; in other words, if the public plan were to have a deductible of $500, they could offer supplementary policies covering the first $500 of medical expenses. How large this business would be would obviously depend on the magnitude of the deductible. Even if it were to be small, some evidence from the U.S. indicates that many people prefer "first-dollar coverage" even when a policy with a modest deductible is considerably cheaper.[1] If most people were to purchase such supplementary policies, the net result in terms of the population coverage would be quite similar to the present system, except for changes in the methods of paying for the insurance. If this were to be the only effect, a reform of this kind would clearly be of limited value.

The more important possibility, however, would be that private-sector insurance firms might start to compete with the public-sector agencies by themselves offering packages equivalent to the basic compulsory insurance, or more comprehensive ones. The extent to which this would happen, would of course crucially depend on the premium setting policies of the public agencies, and we now turn to the question what those policies would be.

Eliminate subsidization of public health insurance

As was briefly noted above, a condition which has to be met if there is going to be effective competition between the public and private sector agencies is that there be no subsidization, implicit or explicit, of the public one. Hence the basic principle in setting premium levels for the compulsory insurance package would be that the expected revenue should be sufficient to cover the total expected cost of the health services covered under the plan. There would obviously be some initial difficulty in finding the actual premium levels which would correspond to this principle. Data on the total cost of all health services used under the present system would provide a starting point. With a substantial deductible, however, a portion of the total cost would now be paid by the patient either directly out of pocket or through supplementary private insurance, and an allowance would have to be made for this in setting premium levels for the compulsory part.

Rates according to risk?

A second issue which would present some difficulty would be that of premium discrimination by risk class. One might argue that the simplest solution would be to have a uniform premium level with no discrimination. As the evidence from the experience with the so-called "community rating" systems in the U.S. indicates, however, this solution presents problems when there is competition from other agencies which use "experience rating", i.e., which discriminate by risk class: those agencies will then be able to offer lower premium levels to individuals who have a low risk of ill health, so that the non-discriminating agency will be left with the high-risk population only. Because of this possibility, it would seem appropriate to allow the public agency to undertake some differentiation by risk class in setting their premiums. Since one of the most important determinants of risk in the health services context is age, in practice this would necessarily mean differential insurance premiums by age, with progressively higher ones for older people. In order to offset the impact that this would have on the net income of the old, it might be required to increase the present degree of income tax discrimination in their favour; I will return to this problem below.

Regulating risk discrimination

An alternative to a discriminatory premium structure in public health insurance would be legislation regulating the amount of premium discrimination which *private* insurance firms would be allowed; such legislation is presently being discussed for the area of automobile insurance, for example. In the limit, private firms could be restricted to offering only one uniform policy as a means of removing their potential competitive advantage over a non-discriminating public agency. There are some arguments against this solution, however. First, non-discriminatory legislation is difficult to enforce; there are ways in which private companies could engage in implicit premium reductions aimed at special groups, especially if they were to offer supplementary insurance in addition to the compulsory plan, and they could focus advertising efforts on special groups, etc. Second, a requirement of uniform premiums would effectively make it possible for an insurance firm (or a prepayment plan) to specialize in providing insurance (and service) for particular age groups. Since the health care needs of the old, for example, are different in character from those of younger people (e.g., families with small children), such specialization might be very efficient. On balance, therefore, I would personally favour a solution in which there *was* discrimination by age, but perhaps with some regulation of the criteria which could be used by private firms in setting their rates.

Enter the private insurers

With public sector insurance premiums set in such a way as to reflect the expected cost of the health services to be used by those insured, as well as the cost of administering the public plan, the field would now be open for private insurance firms to enter the market in competition with it. Any individual would be free to buy his compulsory insurance package either from the public plan, or the equivalent from a private firm. There would have to be some public control to ensure that private policies were indeed at least equivalent to the compulsory requirements, and to ensure that all individuals did in fact have coverage, but the administrative problems in accomplishing this would not seem to be major ones.

Competition with the public plan could emerge from conventional insurance, from institutions of the American Blue Plan type, or from organizations of the pre-paid group practice or health maintenance type. Conventional insurance companies might find it advantageous to offer comprehensive packages which combine the compulsory package with supplementary insurance, rather than offering supplementary insurance alone, or they might be able to offer group plans at lower cost than the public agency. As will be recalled from Chapter Two, the American Blue Plans are based on the principle of contracts between health services providers (physicians and hospitals) and the Plans under which ''participating'' providers agree to provide services to patients covered by the Plan according to a negotiated fee schedule; if the Plans can negotiate lower fees than those charged by independent providers, they might then be able to offer coverage at lower cost.

Health Maintenance Organizations: a form of cheap insurance? The most interesting possibility, however, might be the emergence of competition from prepayment plans of the HMO-type. One of the main conclusions from the discussion in the previous chapters was that a system in which services are provided by independent physicians and hospitals on a fee-for-service basis and in which the population is covered by comprehensive conventional insurance, is likely to produce strong tendencies toward a high rate of health services consumption and a high and rising total cost; attempts at checking these tendencies by various forms of fee control are only going to be partially successful. But if the rate of health services use and the cost of health care in the present system are excessively high in this sense, it would follow for the reasons discussed in Chapter One, that HMO plans should be able to produce comprehensive coverage at lower cost, perhaps substantially lower, than that of conventional insurance.[2]

While at present there do not exist full-blown HMOs in Canada, as I discussed in Chapter Two, a substantial number of group practice arrangements, or HSOs, have nevertheless been started on an experimental basis. If the market for health insurance were to be freed from its present restrictions and made more competitive in the way discussed above, it is reasonable to expect that they would expand in scope, perhaps acquire their own hospital facilities, and develop into more or less complete HMOs along the lines of the U.S. ones. The initiative for the formation of HMOs could also come from other groups. Insurance companies in the group plan market, or labour unions trying to obtain low-cost coverage for their membership, may find it advantageous to enter into prepayment arrangements with hospitals and to hire their own doctors, thus in effect providing insurance through prepayment rather than on a conventional basis. Similarly, groups of doctors might get together to start a prepayment plan; they could secure hospital services by themselves entering into prepayment arrangements with hospitals, or even acquire their own hospitals. Hospitals might hire doctors (part-time or full-time) and start prepayment plans of their own; the possible institutional arrangements are clearly infinite.

Three problems with HMO-type insurance

While the possibility for the owners of HMOs of earning a profit by providing more efficient health care would provide a strong financial incentive for them to become established and grow, one must nevertheless recognize that in practice there are also a number of factors which tend to slow down their development: after all, while HMOs represent an important part of the relatively market-oriented health services system in the U.S., they have by no means taken it over. One of these problems is inherent in the fact that if they are to act as insurance firms as well as health services providers, HMOs can only operate on a relatively large scale. Insurance operates on the basis of the law of large numbers: even if it is highly uncertain what proportion of a *small* population will have a heart attack, say, during a given year, the proportion in a *large* population can be predicted with a small margin of error. Therefore, with a large population, you can be reasonably certain that a premium level (or a prepayment charge) which is fixed on actuarial principles will be enough to cover the cost of treating the heart attacks; in a small population you cannot. Hence, if individual HMOs are to carry out the entire insurance function on their own, they will either have to be established on a fairly large scale or not be established at all.

While this problem may to some extent inhibit effective competition from small-scale HMOs in a market-oriented system, it can partly be resolved through re-insurance. This of course is the way in which small-scale local fire insurance companies, for example, are able to operate: part of their premium revenue is turned over to larger companies in exchange for protection of the local companies against unusually large losses. In a similar way, small-scale HMOs could protect themselves against an unexpectedly high rate of disease incidence among their subscribers by using some of their prepayment revenue for re-insurance with conventional companies. Alternatively, one of the ways in which the emergence of HMOs could be encouraged, in fact, would be through the creation of re-insurance facilities of this kind in the public sector.

A second drawback with health insurance through prepayment arrangements which is often cited is that by its very nature, it restricts the patient's right to choose his own doctor; conventional insurance, of course, does not. My personal opinion is that this objection against prepayment plans does not really have much force. First, with appropriate control on the professional competence of licenced physicians, which is supposed to be ensured by the medical profession itself, the risk of being stuck with an incompetent doctor should presumably not be very great to begin with. Second, with groups of doctors practising together, second opinions are easily accessible, and there will be a strong tendency toward internal quality control. Third, and most important, in a system where conventional insurance and prepayment plans coexist, nobody would be forcing the patient to sign a contract restricting his choice of doctor: he would do so only of his own volition.

It is worth noting that the experiments that are currently going on in Canada with prepaid group practice of the HSO-type include arrangements whereby the patient's right to choose his doctor is not in fact restricted. Under these systems prepayment is made from public insurance to the health centre, but the health centre is billed for charges made when the patient goes to see an outside fee-for-service physician. There is no reason why some version of this kind of arrangement could not be maintained by public-sector insurance plans even in a more market-oriented system. In addition, or as an alternative, the public plan could itself offer a full-fledged prepayment option. In other words, it could offer consumers a choice between, on the one hand, conventional insurance against services rendered by independent doctors and hospitals on a fee-for-service basis, or, on the other hand, insurance against prepayment for those who would be willing to seek their treatment in a public-sector health maintenance organization which had its own hospital facilities and employed its own doctors. It is interesting to note that such an organization would exactly correspond to a national health service in miniature, but with the crucial difference that it would operate in competition with alternative forms of health insurance, either of the conventional kind or of the HMO kind in the private sector. For those who are convinced that a system organized as a publicly-operated national health service is superior to alternative ones, a health services reform along the lines discussed here offers the possibility for this to be demonstrated in competition with alternative methods of health insurance and services provision.

A third often cited reason for skepticism regarding the potential effectiveness of prepayment plans of the HMO-type is that they simply will not emerge on a significant scale under any system, because the medical profession won't stand for them. The evidence from the U.S., which I discussed in Chapter Two, certainly is impressive as a demonstration both of the distaste of American organized medicine for the prepayment alternative and of the effectiveness of its attempts at resisting its growth.

But circumstances differ, and organized medicine in Canada in the late 1970s is in a very different position from that in the U.S. in the 1950s and 1960s. At that time, the involvement of the government, and the degree of public interest, in the health services sector were not major factors, and the medical profession could rely on considerable support for the principle of non-intervention in the process of professional self-regulation of medical practice. At the present time in Canada, it cannot do so to anywhere near the same extent. The principle has already been significantly eroded by the present *de facto* government intervention in the setting of physician fee schedules; and there does not appear to have been significant resistance by organized medicine to the experimental prepayment plans referred to above. Given these developments and the present political climate, I find it difficult to believe that organized medicine would be as successful in Canada as it once was in the U.S., in blocking the growth of such plans provided that people wanted them and governments were prepared to support them. Attempts might be made, and as I have discussed earlier, a well-functioning market mechanism in the health services sector would probably require a considerable amount of political action to preserve effective competition in this and other forms. It seems to me that it is no more unreasonable to hope for success in this endeavour than it is to believe that doctors will accept being put on salary, for example. As I argue in the next section, it is in fact conceivable that in general, physicians would not be opposed to a set of reforms involving greater reliance on the market mechanism.

C. HEALTH SERVICES PROVISION: DOCTORS AND HOSPITALS

How would doctors react to the reform proposals?

To a large extent, the practice of medicine can be taken as independent of the particular features of the organization of the health services system: a good doctor is a good doctor in any system. But the efficiency with which physician manpower is utilized is indeed likely to depend on the way the system is organized; and it has to be used efficiently, because it is expensive: doctors must be paid well enough to compensate them for the cost of their long period of training, and since they can emigrate to other countries, they have to earn enough in Canada to prevent them from moving elsewhere. At the same time, doctors like everybody else are concerned with working conditions as well as with income, and are unlikely to function well in a system they don't like. It is therefore of interest to consider how health care system reform in the direction of more reliance on the market is likely to appear to physicians.

In many ways, it seems to me that a greater reliance on the market mechanism could be expected to produce changes that doctors would welcome. At the present time, a doctor essentially has a choice between straight salaried employment or fee-for-service practice; if he chooses the latter, however, he is in practice subject to fee controls negotiated between the provincial government and his medical association, and many doctors complain about what they feel is excessive government intervention through fee control and general bureaucratic supervision; some are feeling strongly enough about this to seriously contemplate a move to the U.S.

In a system reorganized along the lines we have discussed above, doctors would still have a choice between fee-for-service practice or salaried employment, either in the public sector or perhaps in private health maintenance organizations. In addition, prepaid group practice might become a more common alternative, and there would be no reason why doctors should not be able to combine more than one of these forms. For example, some physicians might choose part-time employment in combination with part-time fee-for-service practice; or individual doctors could work partly on a prepayment and partly on a fee-for-service

171

basis. A market-oriented system would offer a great deal of flexibility in this sense, in contrast to a national health service system, say. Furthermore, with more competition from alternative forms of service delivery, and with patients being directly responsible for a larger share of physician fees, the need for public fee control and supervision under fee-for-service practice would be reduced, i.e., one could expect a bit less "government interference". Some doctors might voluntarily elect to belong to some form of "Blue Plan" under which their fee schedule would be negotiated, but this would be their own choice and not one forced upon them. For others, perhaps especially general practitioners, the task of trying to provide medical care at low cost to those of their patients who are paying their own bills, or to those covered by a prepayment scheme, may present an interesting challenge: in the present system, some GPs have felt that their role has been reduced to that of deciding to what hospital or to what specialist their patients should be referred. This feeling, of course, is consistent with the statistical pattern according to which it has been the cost of hospitalization and specialist referrals that have been the fastest-growing components of health care spending. Revitalization of the general practice function, therefore, might be one of the principal ways through which a market-oriented health services system might contribute to improved efficiency, and it should also fit in well with the renewed interest in this area on the part of medical students in recent years.

The role of organized medicine, i.e., the medical associations, might change in some ways: their function as bargaining agent for the profession in fee negotiations with the public sector would no longer be as important as it currently is. At the same time, with increased competition from prepayment plans or with fee-paying patients being more reluctant to seek medical help, there might be increasing pressure on the associations to undertake measures designed to make fee-for-service practice more competitive, for example by sponsoring insurance of the "Blue Plan" type, or by acting as an information exchange on "prevailing fees". In a system with more competition in this sense, it seems to me that the taboo against publishing fee schedules would be likely to gradually erode away, especially if there is legislative pressure against it, and attempts at upholding it might be replaced instead by efforts at defining what constitutes acceptable methods of price competition.

Organized medicine would of course continue to retain responsibility for the function of "quality control" over physician services, by setting licensing standards and by supervision of the standards of practice among its members; indeed, the latter function might assume even greater importance than it currently has, in a more competitive environment. The problem of regulating the use of nurses and paramedical personnel in order to maintain the quality of care would perhaps also become more important: in a more competitive environment, the incentive for both HMO-type organizations and individual physicians to deliver their services more economically would be stronger.

On balance, should one expect organized medicine to support, or to resist, a reform of the health services system in the direction of a more market-oriented one?

The answer is far from obvious. Perhaps it is fair to say that the medical profession has traditionally been conservative, and at least in principle in favour of "the market"; more accurately, it has been against "government intervention". On the other hand, there exists strong evidence that the introduction of comprehensive, universal, subsidized provincial health insurance plans at least initially had the effect of materially increasing physician incomes.[3] In the last few years, however, incomes of doctors have not risen very fast and public control over medical practice as well as over fees, has become tighter. In short, the future is uncertain, and in some provinces (notably Quebec) the alternative of "putting doctors on salary" is being seriously considered or has been adopted in principle. Support of reforms intended to make the system more efficient and less expensive without sacrificing the traditional independence of the medical profession may seem a reasonable alternative under these circumstances.

The impact of market-oriented reforms on hospital services
In discussing the impact of a more market-oriented health care system on the hospital services industry, it should first of all be noted that the provincial systems of hospital financing in Canada will probably be undergoing some changes in any event. As was discussed in Chapter Two, during the sixties and early seventies,

hospital capacity in Canada was expanding at a rapid rate, as was the cost of both labour and equipment; but government funds were forthcoming, and there was not a great deal of financial restraint to check the expansion. Part of the reason, of course, was the federal-provincial cost-sharing program: when only about half the costs were paid directly out of provincial tax revenue and the rest was distributed among all Canadians through federal taxes, spending money on hospitals must have seemed like a good idea from the viewpoint of the individual provincial government. But this is now changing as money in general is getting tighter and federal-provincial cost-sharing in its original form has been eliminated: checking the hospital cost expansion is now a major provincial priority. The existing budgetary processes under which individual hospitals negotiate with government officials over the details of their budgets is a cumbersome one, however, and decisions on which hospitals to close or what budget items to cut appear to be made in a somewhat arbitrary fashion. As dissatisfaction with this process increases, there will be increasing pressure for more ''rational'' expenditure decisions, and it seems likely to me that in the absence of reform, the system will move in the direction of more centralization: the provinces may ''take over the hospitals''. The U.K. experience clearly supports the notion that it is possible to save money that way. But whether the result would represent a more rational allocation of resources to the production of hospital services than does the present system, is far from clear.

The alternative is to grant more autonomy to individual hospitals while at the same time increasing their responsibility for generating their own revenue. The market-oriented alternative would involve no subsidies from the government: hospitals would be entirely dependent for their revenue on fees-for-service to be paid by individuals or by public or private insurance, or on the income from prepayment arrangements. As discussed previously, some hospitals might be acquired outright by HMO-type organizations: others might operate partly on a fee-for-service basis, partly on the basis of prepayments from group practices. In any case, hospitals would be faced with both patients and doctors shopping for efficient, low-cost service, not just for the highest possible ''quality'' as under the present system. The way in which this might result in a more efficient hospital services industry has already been discussed at some length in the earlier chapters. One type of effect that may be noted here is that it would force hospital managers to adopt more rational principles of cost accounting than those presently used in the budget negotiations with provincial governments. Correspondingly, better cost accounting principles will help the hospitals in establishing a fee structure which corresponds to the real cost of a given service. This fee structure, in turn, would influence the ultimate decisionmakers, i.e., the doctors, and the end result would be more efficient choices of diagnostic and treatment procedures in the light of cost. Under the present system, there are no real incentives for efficient choices in this sense. It is not necessarily the case that doctors deliberately disregard the ultimate cost (to the taxpayer) of their choices: with present reimbursement methods, they simply may not have any idea what the real costs are.

Would a reform of this kind in the hospital services sector necessarily imply that "efficiency" is attained at the cost of sacrificing the smaller hospitals, with the industry becoming concentrated in a small number of large-scale hospitals in the major centres? Not necessarily: a major determinant of the cost of operating a hospital is the range of sophisticated equipment and specialized personnel which it employs. What one could foresee instead might be a tendency for the smaller hospitals to restrict the range of services they provide, rather than closing altogether. Under present financial arrangements in most provinces, furthermore, there is a sharp distinction between short-term acute-care hospitals on the one hand, and institutions for long-term chronic care, convalescent homes and nursing homes, on the other: institutions of the latter kind are often not covered by provincial health insurance whereas the former are. In a market-oriented system, this kind of artificial distinction would disappear, and one could expect the emergence of smaller all-purpose hospitals which would function partly as acute-care hospitals and partly as chronic-care/nursing home institutions.

Finally, whereas a market-oriented system would involve no subsidies to hospitals by federal or provincial governments, there is no reason why individual communities should not be permitted to subsidize the operation of local hospitals if they so desire. Because of the flexibility in terms of the way a "hospital" can operate or be financed, it in fact seems quite possible that the chances of survival of small-town hospitals might be better in a market-oriented system than in a highly centralized one in which the definition of ''efficiency'' is apt to be less imaginative.

IV. SUMMARY: AVENUES OF ACTION

In this section, I first summarize what I consider the major public policy measures that would have to be undertaken in order to make possible a gradual transformation of the Canadian health services system into one in which market forces are allowed to play a major role in the allocation of health resources, as outlined in the previous sections, and briefly touch on some of the practical problems in implementing those policy changes. While these reform proposals to a large extent constitute an integrated package in the sense that they all would have to be implemented together for the system to function in the way I have discussed, a question of obvious interest nevertheless is whether there are partial reform measures which could be worthwhile even in the absence of a complete implementation of the entire package, and I conclude the section with a brief discussion of this question.

A. MAIN REFORM PROPOSALS

i. The fundamental change in the present system which would permit competition to develop in the market for health insurance and health services provision would be *a switch from compulsory subsidized health insurance provided exclusively by the public sector to a system of compulsory but unsubsidized health insurance* which could be obtained from any approved insuring institution either in the public *or* the private sector, either as conventional insurance or in the form of an approved pre-payment plan. The first policy measures which would be required would therefore be to put provincial insurance plans on a premium-financed basis, and to develop criteria for approval of private-sector plans. As discussed above, *those criteria should include provision for a major deductible*.

ii. A switch to premium financing of compulsory health insurance would obviously put an added expenditure burden on individual families, and would be especially difficult for low-income families, or individuals who were bad health risks such as the aged. On the other hand, *the reduction in government expenditure could be used to compensate for this by selective changes in the progressive income tax and in the welfare system.* Present federal-provincial cost-sharing arrangements and income tax legislation might necessitate special arrangements with the federal government for a province to undertake these sorts of changes on its own. The spirit of the recent cost-sharing reform, however, is that each province should be given more freedom to organize its own health care system, and I don't see why it wouldn't be possible for a single province to undertake these changes without the necessity for joint action by all provinces together.

iii. *Modify the present system of hospital financing under which hospitals deliver services on what is essentially a negotiated cost-plus basis, and replace it by one in which services are delivered on the basis of stated fees for individual services, or against prepayment.* Initially, a uniform fee schedule might be negotiated between hospitals and the provincial plans, according to the model of the American Blue Plans. As the system becomes more competitive, however, public-sector negotiation regarding fee schedules may become unnecessary and hospitals could be permitted to set their own fees.

iv. *Legalize health insurance contracts which restrict the patient's right to choose his own doctor, so as to enable prepayment plans to compete with private and public conventional insurance.* Encourage the prepayment alternative by offering a provincial prepayment plan with services provided under contract with private group practices and hospitals, or through a provincially-operated health maintenance organization. Provide public-sector re-insurance facilities for prepayment plans.

The ways in which these four types of health services reform would produce forces rendering the system more efficient have already been discussed at length above. None of them, it seems to me, would represent particularly drastic changes. Hospital financing on a fee-for-service or prepayment basis and the option of individual health insurance through prepayment along the lines suggested here already exist in the U.S. system and have functioned reasonably well there. The most controversial proposal would probably be the first one, i.e., compulsory but wholly premium-financed health insurance, with a deductible. Even if the increased premium-financing were to be offset by tax changes, the proposal would likely be regarded by many as a sacrifice of the principle of equity, because permitting individuals to have major deductibles in their insurance coverage might be thought to conflict with one of the basic conditions for federal cost-sharing discussed in Chapter Two: that provincial health services arrangements must not "impede...reasonable access to necessary medical care, particularly for low-income groups." As I discussed above, I disagree with this view. A reasonable definition of "equity" must imply that everybody should be protected against *unexpectedly* large health care costs in cases of *serious* illness, but not necessarily that "routine" health services should be provided at no direct cost to the patient; hence, it seems to me that the principle of a deductible is not by itself inconsistent with "equity".

B. SOME PROBLEMS OF IMPLEMENTATION

Some of the general problems arising in implementing the various aspects of health services reform listed above have already been briefly touched on in the earlier discussion, and a complete discussion is obviously impossible without a specific set of reform proposals. The purpose here is simply to give some examples of concrete ways in which some of the more important administrative problems could be approached.

An immediate issue that would arise in the conversion of existing provincial plans to a premium basis would be what the levels of premiums would be: since everybody has been covered by subsidized provincial plans, there are no recent actuarial statistics from private firms' experience to go by, neither on disease incidence nor on cost by patient group. On the other hand, existing provincial insurance plan records, or records in provincial ministries of health would provide sources of data from which sample studies of disease incidence and cost of treatment by age of patient could be undertaken. The reduction in the expected cost of health services per patient resulting from a deductible could also be determined from such studies, by constructing frequency distributions of annual costs per patient. The total expected revenue plus expected amounts payable by the patients under a premium structure arrived at in this way could then be checked for consistency with existing data on the total cost of health services, and the premium levels could be compared with data on the cost of similar coverage in the U.S.

Modification of the income tax structure and the welfare system to compensate for higher cost of health insurance and health services to the individual is not difficult in principle but may present an administrative problem in practice. A simple solution might be roughly as follows: all individuals could be given credit against their provincial income tax liability, equivalent to the cost of purchasing comprehensive (i.e., compulsory plus supplementary protection against the deductible portion of the compulsory package) health insurance from the provincial plan, *minus* the premium which would have been payable under the original provincial plan. In this way, the net cost to a patient who does buy comprehensive insurance from the provincial plan would be exactly the same as it would have been without premium reform. The credit would be payable only with proof that the taxpayer did in fact have insurance under an approved plan (i.e., public or private, conventional or prepayment, with or without deductible). To ensure that everybody were covered, the public plan could act as a "default option": anybody not presenting specific proof of insurance would be considered as having coverage under the public plan, and his tax credit would be withheld and paid directly to the plan as a premium.

Reform of the existing system of hospital services financing, finally, would also pose some administrative problems, especially during the transition stage. If the system were to be changed in such a way that hospitals were to be reimbursed according to a uniform fee-for-service schedule, there would first be the problem of designing a rational fee structure: at present Canadian hospitals use accounting methods adapted to the bureaucratic requirements of budget negotiations but inappropriate to the task of measuring the cost of particular services. Again, special costing studies might have to be undertaken to provide a basis for a fee schedule, and again, information from the structure of service fees in the U.S. may be used as partial guidelines. In addition, one would also face the problem whether the fees should be set high enough to enable the least efficient hospitals to break even, in which case the more efficient ones would accumulate substantial surpluses, or conversely, whether it should be geared to the cost structure of the more efficient ones in which case the high-cost hospitals would have to be closed; this may be quite an important problem since at the present time, efficiency and cost varies substantially among Canadian hospitals. A possible compromise solution could be to design an initial schedule which would be too low for the least efficient hospitals, but to offer transitional "adjustment assistance" over a period of several years, which would allow them a reasonable time to improve their efficiency, without, however, forcing the premature closing of hospitals which could become economically viable in the longer run. Again, if the system were to become more competitive, public control over hospital fees could be lifted, and fee determination or prepayment charges left to be negotiated between hospitals and insurance companies or prepayment plans, or to be set directly by the hospitals.

C. AN INTEGRATED PACKAGE
   OR PIECEMEAL REFORM?

As I noted in the introduction, the main areas of health services reform listed above are to a large extent interrelated: if they were to be implemented together, their effects would mutually reinforce each other in producing the potential efficiency advantages of a more market-oriented system. Nevertheless, since the political process is much more likely to work well with more gradual reform, it may be useful to briefly consider the possibility of partial reforms and whether they would be effective at all.

In discussing this issue, a general point that should first be made is that efficiency in the *provision* of health services is to some extent independent of the ultimate source of payment for them. In other words, even in a system where the entire population continues to be covered by comprehensive public-sector health insurance in one form or another, it may still be possible to improve the efficiency of provision. Hence partial reforms such as those proposed under **iii** and **iv** above, i.e., a change in the system of hospital financing and a move toward greater reliance on health services provision through prepayment, may still be worthwhile even if proposal i is not implemented. Consider first hospital accounting and financing (where the need for reform has already been recognized in a number of government reports, most recently in Ontario's Taylor Report[4]): a move toward a structure of uniform reimbursement in the form of given fees for specific services performed would have the same effect in terms of putting pressure on inefficient high-cost hospitals as provincial ministries are at the moment trying to produce through administrative action, and it would transfer the responsibility of reducing cost directly to the hospital managers in a way which the bureaucratic process is unlikely to accomplish.

Similarly, reforms aimed at increasing the reliance on health services provision through prepayment can be undertaken with the system still continuing to rely on universal public-sector health insurance. As noted above, in some provinces experiments are currently going on with physician services being provided by group practices on a prepaid basis. These experiments could be expanded to cover hospital services as well, which would be especially useful if the system of hospital financing had already been modified along the lines just discussed. Experiments could also be conducted by offering individuals a choice between conventional insurance and prepayment, with the premium levels for the two alternatives reflecting actual cost differentials.

Finally, some experimentation could also be undertaken with the principle of deductibles, while in other respects remaining within the framework of the current system. Again, individuals could be given a choice between comprehensive insurance as at present, and an alternative with a deductible at a lower premium cost to reflect the lower expected cost to the public plan. The notion that patients should at least to some extent be responsible for the cost of their health services consumption is currently gaining more and more support in Canada, at least as I read the debate, and as long as individuals are given the choice, it does not seem to me that such a step need be taken to seriously violate the principle of equitable access. At the same time, the results of an experiment along those lines could be very valuable in assessing the probable effects of a more thorough-going set of reforms of the health services system, such as I have outlined in this Chapter.

NOTES

[1][19], pp. 28-30.
[2]See again the evidence summarized in [23].
[3][10], pp. 468-480; also [11].
[4][29], pp. 40-41.

References

[1] Bennett, James E., and Jacques Krasny. "Health Care in Canada: A Series on the Nation's Health," reprint from *Financial Post*, March 26-May 7, 1977.

[2] Berg, R. L., ed. *Health Status Indexes*. Chicago, Hospital Research and Educational Trust, 1973.

[3] Canada, Department of Health and Welfare. *Health Field Indicators*. Ottawa, Department of Health and Welfare, December 1976.

[4] Canada. *Task Force Report on the Costs of Health Services in Canada: Vol. 3, Health Services*. Ottawa, Queen's Printer, 1970.

[5] Canadian Medical Association, Statistics, Systems and Economic Research Unit. *Quickbase*. Ottawa, Canadian Medical Association, June 1978.

[6] Central Office of Information. *Health Services in Britain*. London, British Information Services, No. R5154/77, September 1977.

[7] Cooper, M. H. *Rationing Health Care*. New York, Wiley, 1975.

[8] Culyer, A. *Measuring Health: Lessons for Ontario,* O.E.C. Research Studies, No. 14. Toronto, Ontario Economic Council, 1978.

[9] Dyck, Frank J., *et al* "Effect of Surveillance on the Number of Hysterectomies in the Province of Saskatchewan," *New England Journal of Medicine,* Vol. 296, June 9, 1977, pp. 1326-1328.

[10] Evans, Robert G., "Beyond the Medical Market Place: Expenditure, Utilization and Pricing of Insured Health Care in Canada," in Richard N. Rosett, ed., *The Role of Health Insurance in the Health Services Sector*. New York, National Bureau of Economic Research, 1976, pp. 437-492.

[11] Evans, Robert G. *et al.* "Medical Productivity, Scale Effects and Demand Generation," *Canadian Journal of Economics,* Vol. 4, Aug. 1973, pp. 376-393.

[12] Feldstein, M. "Hospital Cost Inflation: A Study of Non-Profit Dynamics," *American Economic Review,* Vol. 61, Dec. 1971, pp. 853-872.

[13] Glaser, W. A. *Paying the Doctor*. Baltimore, Johns Hopkins Press, 1970.

[14] Heung, Raymond. *The Do's and Don'ts of Housing Policy*. Vancouver, The Fraser Institute, 1977.

[15] Information Canada. *The Community Health Centre in Canada*. Ottawa, Health Centre Project, 1972.

[16] International Monetary Fund. *International Financial Statistics*. Washington, International Monetary Fund, Volume XXXI, No. 8, August 1978.

[17] Kessel, Reuben. "Price Discrimination in Medicine," *Journal of Law and Economics,* Vol. 1, No. 1, 1958, pp. 20-53.

[18] Knowles, John H., ed. *Doing Better and Feeling Worse; Health in the United States,* New York, Norton, 1977.

[19] Krizay, J. and A. Wilson. *The Patient as Consumer,* Lexington, Mass., Toronto, London, D. C. Heath, 1974.

[20] Lalonde, Marc. *A New Perspective on the Health of Canadians; A Working Document,* Ottawa, Information Canada, 1975.

[21] Leclair, Maurice. "The Canadian Health Care System," in *National Health Insurance: Can We Learn From Canada?*, ed. by S. Andreopoulos. New York, Wiley, 1975.

[22] Lewis, Charles E. "Variations in the Incidence of Surgery," *New England Journal of Medicine,* Vol. 281, No. 6, Oct. 16, 1969, pp. 880-884.

[23] Luft, H. S. "How do Health Maintenance Organizations Achieve Their Savings: Rhetoric and Evidence," *New England Journal of Medicine,* Vol. 298, No. 24, June 15, 1978, pp. 1336-1343.

[24] Maxwell, Robert. *Health Care: The Growing Dilemma,* Second edition, New York, McKinsey and Company, June 1975.

[24A] Migué, Jean-Luc and Gerard Bélanger. *The Price of Health,* English edition. Toronto, Macmillan of Canada, 1974.

[25] Newhouse, J. "Toward a Theory of Non-Profit Institutions: An Economic Model of a Hospital," *American Economic Review,* Vol. 60, March 1970, pp. 64-73.

[26] Pauly, M. and M. Redisch. "The Not-For-Profit Hospital as a Physician Cooperative," *American Economic Review,* Vol. 63, March 1973, pp. 87-99.

[26A] Pratt, Lois. *Family Structure and Effective Health Behavior,* Boston, Houghton Mifflin Company, 1976.

[27] OECD. *Organization for Change: The British National Health Service,* Paris, 1975.

[28] OECD. *Public Expenditure on Health,* Studies in Resource Allocation No. 4. Paris, July 1977.

[29] Ontario. *Report of the Joint Advisory Committee of the Government of Ontario and the Ontario Medical Association on Methods to Control Health Care Costs.* Toronto, mimeograph, Dec. 29, 1977.

[29A] Smith, Adam. *The Wealth of Nations.* Homewood, Richard D. Irwin, Inc., 1963 (original edition 1776).

[29B] Schwartz, W. B. and Komesar, N. K. "Doctors, Damages and Deterrence", *New England Journal of Medicine,* Vol. 298, No. 23, June 8, 1978, pp. 1282-1289.

[30] Soderstrom, Lee. *The Canadian Health System.* London, Croom-Helm, 1978.

[31] Statistics Canada. *Hospital Morbidity, 1973,* Cat. C.S. 82-206.

[32] Statistics Canada. *Hospital Statistics, 1974,* Cat. C.S. 83-217.

[33] Statistics Canada. *National Accounts and Expenditure Accounts, 1961-75,* Cat. C.S. 13-201.

[34] Statistics Canada. *Population Estimates by Marital Status, Age and Sex, for Canada and Provinces,* Cat. C.S. 91-203, Annual (1972); and *Population of Canada and the Provinces by Sex and Age Group,* Cat. C.S. 91-202, Annual (1973, 74, 75).

[35] Statistics Canada. *Surgical Procedures and Treatments, 1973, 1974,* Cat. C.S. 82-208, Annual.

[36] Statistics Canada. *Vital Statistics, Vol. III, Deaths, 1973,* Cat. C.S. 84-206.

[37] Statistics Canada. *Vital Statistics, Vol. III, Deaths, 1974,* Cat. C.S. 84-206.

[38] Tengstam, A. *Patterns of Health Care and Education in Sweden.* Paris, OECD Centre for Educational Research and Innovation, 1975.

[39] United Kingdom, Central Statistical Office. *Annual Abstract of Statistics.* London, Her Majesty's Stationery Office, 1975.

[40] United Kingdom, Central Statistical Office. *Annual Abstract of Statistics.* London, Her Majesty's Stationery Office, 1976.

[41] United Kingdom, Central Statistical Office. *Social Trends, No. 5, 1974.* London, Her Majesty's Stationery Office, 1974.

[42] United States, United States Bureau of the Census. *Statistical Abstract of the United States: 1976.* (97th Edition.) Washington, D.C., 1976.

[43] United States, Department of Health, Education and Welfare. *Medical Care Expenditures, Prices and Costs: Background Book.* Washington Social Security Administration, Office of Research and Statistics, September 1975.

[44] United States, Department of Health, Education and Welfare. *Compendium of National Health Expenditures Data,* compiled by B.S. Cooper, N. L. Worthington, and M. F. McGee. Washington, Social Security Administration, Office of Research and Statistics, No. SSA 76-11927, January 1976.

[45] Weinstein, M. C., and W. B. Stason. *Hypertension: A Policy Perspective.* Cambridge University Press, Cambridge, Mass. and London, Harvard U.P., 1976.

[46] World Bank. *World Tables 1976.* Baltimore, Johns Hopkins University Press, 1976.

the fraser institute

Member of the Association of Canadian Publishers and the Canadian Booksellers Association

BOOKS IN PRINT

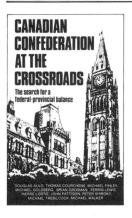

A timely
book on
Canada's
future...

CANADIAN CONFEDERATION AT THE CROSSROADS
The Search for a Federal-Provincial Balance

The eleven Fraser Institute authors examine carefully the extent to which the current allocation of powers and functions in the Canadian system of government serves the economic and cultural interests of all Canadians. Since the issues raised involve many aspects of our society, the book spans the broad mosaic of Canadian life from economic policy to legal uniformity; from broadcasting to urban development policy.

Canadian Confederation at the Crossroads: The Search for a Federal-Provincial Balance asks whether much of what is interpreted as **separatist** sentiment in Quebec in fact represents a deeply-rooted reaction to a rising feeling of alienation from government: a reaction as strongly rooted in the West and the Maritimes as in Quebec. As a solution, this book therefore looks at the ways personal and regional independence can be achieved within the framework of our existing constitutional structure. Can we produce a workable and acceptable federal-provincial balance that will reinvigorate our confederation?

Authors include: **Michael Walker,** Director, the Fraser Institute (Introduction); **Perrin Lewis,** Assistant Economic Adviser, Bank of Nova Scotia, Toronto (on the tangled tale of taxes and transfers); **John C. Pattison,** Assistant Professor, School of Business Administration, University of Western Ontario (on dividing the power to regulate); **Thomas J. Courchene,** Professor of Economics, University of Western Ontario (on the transfer system and regional disparities); **Peter Shiroky,** Fraser & Beatty, Toronto and **Michael Trebilcock,** Director, Law & Economics Programme, University of Toronto (on the uniformity of law); **Pierre Lortie,** Executive Vice-president SECOR, Inc., Montreal (on education, broadcasting, and language policy); **Douglas A. Auld,** Professor of Economics, University of Guelph (on fiscal policy); **Brian A. Grosman,** Professor of Law, University of Saskatchewan and **Michael J. Finley,** Legal Research Officer, Law Reform Commission of Saskatchewan (on law enforcement); and **Michael A. Goldberg,** Professor & Chairman, Urban Land Economics Division, Faculty of Commerce & Business Administration, University of British Columbia (on housing and urban development policy).

381 Pages
10 Tables
33 pages of extensive notes and bibliographical references
$9.95 paperback ISBN 0-88975-025-4

Books on Current Economic Issues

THE SCIENCE COUNCIL'S WEAKEST LINK
A Critique of the Science Council's Technocratic Industrial Strategy for Canada

The Science Council of Canada recently published a study by two of its researchers—"The Weakest Link"—which purports to prove that the root of the country's economic malaise can be found in the "technological underdevelopment of Canadian industry." One solution, the Council's book proposes, is the adoption of an "Industrial Strategy" based on "technological sovereignty" involving wide-ranging and potentially massive intervention by government in the country's industrial structure.

Because the Science Council's views on Industrial Strategy are acquiring increasing attention in government policy circles and what many believe to be a credibility that is undeserved, this Fraser Institute book, by Kristian Palda, a Queen's University Professor of Business Economics, represents a searching critique of what is becoming the "Science Council view"; as such, it is a particularly useful contribution to the on-going debate about one of the most fundamental issues of our time.

73 Pages	6 Charts	7 Tables	$4.95 paperback	ISBN 0-88975-031-9

UNEMPLOYMENT INSURANCE
Global Evidence of its Effects on Unemployment

This book contains thirteen papers originally presented at an **International Conference** held in Vancouver. The proceedings begin with a broad, non-technical examination by the two editors, **Herbert G. Grubel**, Professor of Economics, Simon Fraser University and **Michael A. Walker**, Director of the Fraser Institute, of the relationship between "moral hazard", unemployment insurance and the rate of unemployment.

In Parts One and Two, the participating economists examine, empirically and theoretically, contemporary experience of national programs for dealing with unemployment in nine countries: in the **United States (Daniel S. Hamermesh); Canada (Ronald G. Bodkin** and **André Cournoyer); New Zealand (Geoff P. Braae); Sweden (Ingemar Stähl); Belgium (M. Gerard, Herbert Glejser** and **J. Vuchelen); Ireland (Brendan M. Walsh); France (Emil-Maria Claassen** and **Georges Lane); Federal Republic of Germany (H. König** and **Wolfgang Franz); and Italy, (Paolo Onofri** and **Anna Stagni).**

In Part Three, to add an historical perspective, two papers examine British social insurance systems—the 19th century Poor Laws **(Stephen T. Easton)** and the unemployment relief of the 1918-1939 inter-war period **(Daniel K. Benjamin** and **Levis A. Kochin)**. This Part also contains an econometric study of unemployment insurance programs across a number of countries **(Dennis Maki** and **Zane Spindler)**.

In addition to the delivered papers, the book contains provocative discussions by an international roster of economists who commented on the formal proceedings: **Melvin Reder; Erwin Diewert; John Helliwell; Stephen M. Hills; Michel Bergeron; Joseph E. Hight; Angus Maddison; Ernst Berndt; Louis Jacobson; Martin Feldstein; Samuel Brittan** and **John Cragg**. The informal discussions are summarized by **Sandra S. Christensen.**

400 Pages	21 Charts	18 pages of extensive bibliographical references and notes
82 tables		$12.95 paperback ISBN 0-88975-008-4

PROVINCIAL GOVERNMENT BANKS
A Case Study of Regional Response to National Institutions

Can national financial institutions, such as banks, function in a country as regionally diverse as Canada without seeming to discriminate between the regions? Were the complaints of the four Western Premiers at the Western Economic Opportunities Conference in Calgary justified? If there is discrimination, would the proposed provincial government "B.C. Savings and Trust" super bank provide relief from it? What would be the cost of such relief? This book, by **John Benson** of the Economics Department at the University of Guelph, considers a very real and specific aspect of the sharing of regulatory power within Confederation. Professor Benson was invited by the Fraser Institute to examine the B.C. super bank to see to what extent it is justified. His case study provides a useful contribution to the current debate about the regional impact of national institutions and should commend itself to all Canadians concerned with the economics of Confederation.

136 Pages   12 Tables $3.95 paperback   ISBN 0-88975-020-3

OIL IN THE SEVENTIES
Essays on Energy Policy

Edited by **G. Campbell Watkins,** President, DataMetrics Limited, Calgary and Visiting Professor of Economics, University of Calgary and **Michael Walker,** Director of the Fraser Institute.

In Part One, *Energy in the Marketplace,* contributors include **Russell S. Uhler** of the University of British Columbia (on economic concepts of petroleum energy supply); **Ernst R. Berndt** of the University of British Columbia (on Canadian energy demand and economic growth); and **G. Campbell Watkins** (on Canadian oil and gas pricing).

In Part Two, *Government in the Marketplace,* contributors include **Walter J. Mead** of the University of California, Santa Barbara (on private enterprise, regulation and government enterprise in the energy sector); and **Edward W. Erickson** of North Carolina State University and **Herbert S. Winokur, Jr.,** of Harvard University (on international oil and multi-national corporations).

In Part Three, *Oil in the Seventies: Policies and Prospects,* contributors include **G. David Quirin** and **Basil A. Kalymon,** both of the University of Toronto (on the financial position of the petroleum industry) and **James W. McKie** of the University of Texas at Austin (on United States and Canadian energy policy).

320 Pages   17 Charts   25 Tables   Index
$3.95 paperback ISBN 0-88975-011-4 $14.95 hardcover ISBN 0-88975-018-1

FRIEDMAN ON GALBRAITH
. . . and on curing the British Disease

Why is it that **John Kenneth Galbraith's** theories have become widely accepted by the general public when there is almost a total lack of support for them in the economics profession? Is Galbraith a *scientist or a missionary?* **Milton Friedman,** Nobel Laureate in Economics 1976, addresses these and other questions about Galbraith as economist and prophet in this Fraser Institute book. Whatever the reader's view of Galbraith, this book by Friedman is must reading. It is said that Canada and other countries are on the same path as Britain—to some, the *British Disease* is the logical ending of Galbraith's story. In the second essay in this book, Professor Friedman outlines a cure for the British Disease: the principles that Friedman develops in this essay are of immediate Canadian interest as they point out the necessity to adopt gradualist corrective policies *now* before the more jarring policies currently required in the U.K. are necessary here.

66 Pages $3.95 paperback   ISBN 0-88975-015-7

HOW MUCH TAX DO YOU REALLY PAY?
Introducing the Canadian Consumer Tax Index

Have you ever stopped to think what you pay your federal, provincial, and municipal governments in taxes? Have you ever wondered how much hidden tax you pay on all of the things you buy? This Fraser Institute Guide asks and answers two basic questions: Q: Who pays for government? (A: You do!) and Q: How much do you pay? By reading this book, you will see for the first time how astronomically the Canadian CONSUMER TAX INDEX has risen over the past fifteen years. And if you want to, you can actually calculate how much tax you really pay and your real tax rate.

120 Pages   6 Charts   22 Tables $2.95 paperback   ISBN 0-88975-004-1

THE ILLUSION OF WAGE AND PRICE CONTROL
Essays on Inflation, its Causes and its Cures

A look at the causes of inflation and an examination of responses to it in Canada, the United States and the United Kingdom. Contributors include **Jack Carr, Michael Darby, Jackson Grayson, David Laidler, Michael Parkin, Robert Schuettinger** and **Michael Walker**.

258 Pages   16 Charts   7 Tables
$5.95 paperback ISBN 0-88975-001-7 $2.95 pocketbook ISBN 0-88975-005-X

WHICH WAY AHEAD?
Canada after Wage and Price Control

This book draws together the research and ideas of fifteen well-informed Canadian economists. It presents a remarkable concurrence of views on the controls program, its effectiveness and on the causes of inflation. The book suggests policies best suited to give Canada a healthy and internationally-competitive economy. It discusses the need for restraint in the public sector; it proposes policies to meet the critical double-headed challenge of low inflation and full employment. Contributors are: **Douglas Auld, Jack Carr, Louis Christofides, Thomas Courchene, James W. Dean, John Floyd, Herbert Grubel, John Helliwell, Stephan Kaliski, David Laidler, Richard Lipsey, Michael Parkin, Simon Reisman, Grant Reuber** and **Michael Walker**.

376 Pages   5 Charts   9 Tables $4.95 paperback   ISBN 0-88975-010-6

THE REAL COST OF THE BC MILK BOARD
A Case Study in Canadian Agricultural Policy

Two Simon Fraser University professors of economics, **Herbert Grubel** and **Richard Schwindt**, analyze the social cost of the B.C. milk marketing board, the impact of the milk quota system and the extent to which the Board transfers income from consumers to producers. Grubel and Schwindt develop an analytical framework that can be applied to marketing boards in general. Their study documents the consequences of marketing boards and has been published to stimulate public discussion of the important economic issues at stake.

78 Pages   6 Charts   6 Appendices $3.95 paperback   ISBN 0-88975-013-0

Housing & Land Economics Series

PROFITS IN THE REAL ESTATE INDUSTRY

A controversial question never far from the headlines is the subject of profits in the real estate industry. In this book—the fifth in the Fraser Institute's housing and land economics series—**Basil Kalymon** of the University of Toronto's Faculty of Management Studies concludes that profits in real estate do not significantly deviate from those earned in investments in other industries. Kalymon examines the question in a scholarly and highly readable manner and vigorously enters the debate on equity compensation and the comparative performance of publicly-owned real estate companies and developers vis-à-vis other sectors of Canadian industry.

| 59 Pages | 8 Tables | $2.95 paperback | ISBN 0-88975-016-5 |

PUBLIC PROPERTY?
The Habitat Debate Continued

Essays on the price, ownership and government of land. Edited by **Lawrence B. Smith,** Associate Chairman, Department of Political Economy University of Toronto and **Michael Walker,** Director of the Fraser Institute.

Twelve Canadian economists examine the operation and importance of land markets and the impact of government regulation, control and ownership on the supply and price of land. Essential reading for all those concerned with the future of landownership in Canada.

Contributors include: **David Nowlan** of the University of Toronto (on the land market and how it works); **Larry R. G. Martin** of the University of Waterloo (on the impact of government policies on the supply and price of land for urban development); **Stanley W. Hamilton** and **David E. Baxter,** both of the University of British Columbia (on government ownership and the price of land); **Jack Carr** and **Lawrence Smith,** both of the University of Toronto (on public land banking and the price of land); **James R. Markusen** and **David T. Scheffman,** both of the University of Western Ontario (on ownership concentration in the urban land market); **Stuart McFadyen** of the University of Alberta and **Robert Hobart** of the Ministry of State for Urban Affairs (on the foreign ownership of Canadian land) and **Michael A. Goldberg** of the University of British Columbia (on housing and land prices in Canada and the U.S.).

278 Pages   7 Charts   20 Tables
$5.95 paperback ISBN 0-88975-014-9 $12.95 hardcover ISBN 0-88975-017-3

RENT CONTROL—A POPULAR PARADOX
Evidence on the Economic Effects of Rent Control

Eleven essays on the economics of housing in Canada and on the effects of rent control in the United States, the United Kingdom, Austria, France and Sweden by Nobel Prize winners in economics, **F. A. Hayek,** and **Milton Friedman,** and **George Stigler, Bertrand de Jouvenel, F. W. Paish, F. G. Pennance, E. O. Olsen, Sven Rydenfelt** and **Michael Walker.**

| 230 Pages | 9 Charts | 28 Tables | $2.95 pocketbook | ISBN 0-88975-007-6 |

ANATOMY OF A CRISIS
Canadian Housing Policy in the Seventies

In this book **Lawrence B. Smith,** Associate Chairman of the Department of Political Economy at the University of Toronto, and one of Canada's leading urban economists, considers the content and objectives of Federal housing policies from 1935 to the present. His conclusions that 1) housing policy is more and more being used as a vehicle for redistributing income in Canada and 2) that this policy is at the same time destroying the private sector's incentive and ability to supply housing, make the book required reading for everybody concerned with housing in Canada today. The book contains a comprehensive bibliography.

55 Pages   7 Tables $3.95 paperback   ISBN 0-88975-009-2

THE DO'S AND DON'TS OF HOUSING POLICY
The Case of British Columbia

Economist **Raymond Heung's** book is a case study of housing in British Columbia. As well as taking vigorous issue with the methodology and conclusions of the Jaffary and Runge reports, (issued as a result of a B.C. government-funded Interdepartmental Study), Heung's book provides a useful and detailed framework for housing market analysis, together with an examination of the costs of adopting a housing allowance scheme for British Columbia. This scheme, guaranteeing access to basic accommodation for all residents in the province, would cost less than half as much as current government outlays on housing in the province. The book, written by a former staff member of the government study team, has a message applicable to every province. As such, it should be of interest to everyone concerned with Canadian housing economics.

145 Pages   4 Charts   28 Tables $8.00 paperback   ISBN 0-88975-006-8

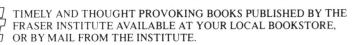 TIMELY AND THOUGHT PROVOKING BOOKS PUBLISHED BY THE
FRASER INSTITUTE AVAILABLE AT YOUR LOCAL BOOKSTORE,
OR BY MAIL FROM THE INSTITUTE.

BOOK ORDER FORM

To: The Fraser Institute,
     626 Bute Street,
     Vancouver, British Columbia,
     Canada. V6E 3M1

Please send me:

_____ copies of _____

_____ copies of _____

_____ copies of _____

Please add $1.00 for postage and handling

Enclosed is my payment in full of $ _____ or charge to:

Visa # _____

Mastercharge # _____

Expiry Date: _____

Signature: _____

Please send me information about membership in the
   Fraser Institute . . . . ☐

please print

Name: _____

Title: _____

Organization: _____

Address: _____

_____

_____

please include postal code